HAZING

HAZING

An Anthology of True Hazing Tales
Edited by Bob Wingate

the Outbound Press INC.

New York

Hazing
An Anthology of True Hazing Tales

First Edition 1994

ISBN 0-9640291-0-03

Manufactured in the United States of America

Published by The Outbound Press, Inc.
89 Fifth Avenue, Suite 803
New York, NY 10003

CONTENTS

INTRODUCTION

By John Beatty
Professor of Anthropology, Brooklyn College

Rituals which mark changes of status occur in all human societies, and probably have ever since prehistoric times. Many of these rituals revolve around "life cycle" changes. Rituals which mark birth, the attainment of adult status, marriage and death are common in many societies.

Technically rituals which mark changes of status are known as rites of passage. The first serious analysis of these particular rituals was done by Van Gennep (1960) who derived the term from rites marking physical, rather than a strictly social or psychological passage. He expanded the meaning to a broader area, and concentrated largely on the latter.

Van Gennep postulated that there were three steps in the rituals: separation, transition and integration. The first of these is used to remove the initiate from his old status, the last is used to integrate the initiate into his new status. The middle phase, known technically as the rite of transition, places the initiate into a kind of "betwixt and between" state, in which he is in limbo. Anthropologists, using a term derived from the Greek word for the threshold of a doorway, have coined the term "liminal" to refer to this stage.

In addition to the rituals which mark life cycle changes, there are also those which occur when a person becomes a member of a group. Entrance into a society of some sort is often characterized by one or more rites of passage known as initiations.

Although strictly speaking, initiations constitute only the third of the three parts of the ritual, that of incorporation, the term is often used loosely to cover the entire process. The most intensively studied aspect of these rituals has been the transition phase which corresponds more closely to what is seen as the "hazing" phase of the process (see such works as La Fontaine, Turner, etc.). In fraternities and similar organizations, this middle phase occurs when the initiates have a quasi-status—that is they are not strictly outsiders, nor are they fully insiders yet.

Although there are some societies found in the world for women, by and large it is the men's societies about which more has been written. While it has been argued that men's societies receive most attention because most anthropologists are men, there is a growing body of evidence to show that men seem to be more involved with these kinds of associations.

There seems to be no limit to the number of different kinds of societies that exist, but the ones that stand out most in terms of initiations are those which mark entrance into manhood and those which are involved in secret societies.

Of course, not all societies have complex initiations into adult status. American society by and large lacks these rituals. For some, a bar mitzvah or confirmation fills the bill. In the days when the draft was still in use, there were many whose initiation into manhood was that institution known as boot camp, and basic training to a large degree served the function of a typical initiation into manhood. The inductee was separated from his family and the world he knew (separation), placed in a state of limbo (boot camp) and finally integrated into his new status—that of a full fledged member of the armed forces. Even within these groups there may be further rituals marking advancing status. Airborne training, for example, is a kind of rite of passage for soldiers becoming paratroopers.

Without a doubt, many of the associations for which there are initiations are known as secret societies, although it is necessary to make a distinction between true secret societies and "societies with secrets." In the former, it is the membership which is secret. The activities of the group may not be. In the latter, the membership is often known—what the members do (or at least some aspect of what they do) is secret,

Secret societies have many functions in different parts of the world. Sometimes they are the official administrators of justice, and membership may be seen as secret so that the judge can operate freely. Constraints of kinship and friendship can be set aside without a breach in the actual relationship between the participants. In some instances, secret societies may be criminal. To some degree one can consider organized crime, certain supremacist movements, and terrorist organizations (without trying to decide who is and who is not a terrorist!) to be secret societies.

Fraternal organizations like the Masons, and the Greek organizations at colleges are examples of "societies with secrets." In these organizations, members often wear jackets with their affiliations clearly marked on them. There are, however, certain rituals that the organization performs which are kept from the general public. Masons, for example, often wear rings and other markers of their affiliation. They may perform charitable works quite openly. They have, however, a ritual (or set of rituals) which is not open to the public and may be seen only by fully initiated masons.

In many cases initiates are given "secret knowledge" which is of crucial import. In the ancient "mystery" cults, with their esoteric initiations, this secret knowledge was of critical importance.

In other societies, the common rites of passage are those that occur into adult status. These often involve a variety of things done to the initiates. These may include ritual tattooing, scarification, the knocking out of a tooth, circumcision (see Saitoti 1986) and subincision (the opening of the penis lengthwise to the depth of the urethra. This last has been well described and documented. Bruno Bettelheim (1959) published an elaborate analysis of the symbolism of this particular aspect of mutilation. In his book *Society of the Flutes*, Herdt discusses one society in New Guinea in which young men are sodomized as part of their initiation.

Western society has produced a number of initiation ceremonies which are largely involved in joining a specific group. The group in effect "tests" its potential members before allowing them to enter and thereby gain the benefits of the organization. The only such ceremony that seems not to have that function has to do with those initiations involved in "crossing the line" — that is, the ceremonies done on board ships when crossing the equator, the arctic circle or other significant places. These are well documented in Henning Henningsen's book, *Crossing the Equator*.

Most of the time, the organizations offer something special to their members. In much older times, the initiation into the various "mysteries" offered secret knowledge. Much has been made of late of the esoteric knowledge hidden in certain religious sects (like the Essenes). Just what that knowledge is or was seems somewhat unclear. Later groups, such as the Knights Templar, and what may be their lineal descendants, the Masons, also are believed by many to possess secret information which gives people power, money, prestige, and so on. The Masons, Rosicrucians, and, to a lesser degree, the Knights of Columbus and Knights of Pythias, fall into this category, although the latter seem to have less the feeling of mysticism about them than the first two do.

Fraternal organizations such as fraternities, and the less mystical fraternal organizations mentioned above, along with the military, or certain "elite" branches such as the Airborne, SEALS, Green Berets, etc., are also known for some hazing-type events before full acceptance is granted to the members. The fact that people in many of these societies begin to make contacts with other people who are, or are likely to become, influential, explains some of the desire both to be a member as well as the attempts to restrict membership to a select few. *Goat Brothers*, a book by Larry Colton, gives some glimpse into how this procedure operates by following the lives of five brothers in a fraternity in the 1960's and what develops in their lives thereafter.

Athletic teams also have on occasion a kind of initiation for incoming members. These, like those of fraternities, and to some degree those in the military and military schools, have come under heavy scrutiny because of the number of injuries and occasional deaths. There are several books available dealing with initiations into fraternities, such as Leemon's *Rites of Passage in Student Culture*.

A recent book, *Broken Pledges*, by Hank Nuwer (1990), for example, details a number of accidents which occurred during hazings and in circumstances involving fraternities. A recent case in the State of Washington involved a wrestler who was sodomized by other members of the team with a broomstick. These kinds of events have tended to make pledging and hazing practices some-what anathema of late, although little seems to go wrong in the initiations of groups such as the Masons, etc., where, in the tradition of initiations in the past and in other cultures, the format of the initiation is pretty well set and is not something easily modified by someone whose interests lie in a more dangerous area. Fraternity and military initiations tend to be rather freewheeling in their approach and so there is perhaps a greater danger that things might get out of control.

Recently, we have seen the development of a kind of "cult of manhood," a thesis which has been put forth by Robert Bly (1990) for what has come to be known as the "men's movement." Bly's interview with Bill Moyers's "A Gathering of Men" has done much to bring about a return to rituals designed to try to produce a kind of male bonding. There have even appeared some "how to do it" books like Bill Kauth's *A Circle of Men*, which detail how to put together a men's group, while others such as Ray Raphael's *The Men from the Boys* attempts a more theoretical analysis of the desires of men to become involved in such groups. These recent approaches tend to try to create a bonding through typically male activities (hunting, warfare—see paint pellet games, for example) or something somewhat more mystical, tied in some way to American Indian vision quests.

Whatever the basic underlying psychological or sociological motives involved, it does appear that more and more men have become interested in finding ways to bond or test themselves in an age in which gender role identification is becoming less and less clear. This kind of testing, so typical of many initiations and hazings, seems to have an appeal to many men whose involvement is far more gender based than sexually based. That is to say, many perceive it as an aspect of masculinity without connotations of eroticism.

ADOLESCENT INITIATIONS

ACADEMY HAZE DAYS

🏛

Off the top of my head, I can think of at least 20 friends from Academy life who had to undergo forced bondage. It was certainly a long held rite of passage where I went to school. Plebes knew how to suffer back in the 60's.

The plebes in my building lived on the second floor and one night every plebe on the floor was bound and gagged in our underwear or less. About a half-hour before lights out, my room-mate Fager and I were next door studying and shooting shit with our neighbors Capwell and Nuell when we heard yelling and hollering up and down the corridor. Upperclassmen were running wild, bursting through every door and seizing plebes left and right. They grabbed the four of us and practically tore our clothes off. Everyone was stripped to the waist with Fager, Capwell and a few others totally naked. All plebes were gagged. I received a ball of cloth in my mouth and a strip of tape over my lips. Fager got his underwear back the hard way, stuffed in his mouth with a rag tied round his head.

We were all pronounced the lowest shits ever to disgrace the South and the Academy. In a minute, rope was everywhere. Some cadets carried it in their hands, others lifted or took off their shirts to get to the rope coiled around their bodies. My hands and feet were tied up along with all the other plebes. They pushed me on the floor next to Fager and Nuell, and we struggled against the bonds in tandem. A few plebes, including Capwell, were dragged away to the upperclass floor, where they endured belt whippings and cigarette burns on their bare butts. Capwell said he was whipped while his hands were tied to an overhead pole. And back on the plebe floor, half naked plebes writhed on the linoleum, half in and half out of doorways, struggling to untie ourselves and hide the occasional hard on. Hell Week, nicknamed Haze Days, had come to the Academy.

That was the signal for a horde of abuse and hazing, in an effort to break the plebes' spirits, or as the ringleader Cadet Rexford put it, "to separate the men from the shits." Plebes had to do all kinds of extra duty and zillions of laps and pushups, and acted as personal servants and houseboys for the needs of the upperclass cadets. But cadets were likely to drag a plebe behind a fence and piss on him, or tie him to a tree, or strip him and make him march naked on the parade ground. Bondage was reserved for special cases. Some plebes were singled out because they opposed the Vietnam War, or they were Jewish, or their fathers weren't rich enough. Capwell and Nuell were tied up naked in the shower because Nuell was a liberal. Rexford and two other cadets, Hunt and McDermott, liked to beat up and tie up "free thinkers", and one night they broke into our room and tied us to our beds. We were gagged and beaten with their leather belts after they pulled our pants down. Fager had it worse than me. His name was pronounced FAY-ger but Rexford dubbed him FAGG-er or just "Faggot." He wasn't effeminate but had what they used to call "an artistic temperament" with a coverboy face, and that didn't help. The next day, I was doing an errand for a cadet and had to go to the toolshed. Fager was there, naked from the waist down, tied and gagged on a saw horse with "faggot" written on his ass. Rexford and another cadet, Nichols, had dragged Fager into the shed to paddle his ass and left him tied up as the school faggot with his ass available for anyone's use. I untied Fager, but when Rexford found out, Fager and I were taken to the football field and tied to a goalpost during practice. The soccer team was on the field, and they acted as if nothing was wrong.

There were organized hazing activities at the Academy, some downright painful, but they were genteel compared to the random acts of torture carried out mainly by Rexford and his friends. But the scariest part was that plebes were known to disappear for the night, usually in twos. It happened to Capwell and Nuell next door. They'd been missing the night before but weren't on report, and the next day were super quiet and extra subservient to Rexford and the others, but they wouldn't talk about it, not even to Fager and me.

We found out why that night. Fager and I were snatched on the way back from study group. Rexford and McDermott forced Fager to the pavement, while Hunt and Nichols pushed me against a wall. My hands were tied and I was gagged with a rolled up rag, then I was blindfolded and one of them tied a burlap sack over my head. The cadets picked me up and put me inside a station wagon or a van, and something that smelled like oilcloth was put on top of me. I felt something warm against my back and knew it must be Fager. I could feel him struggling and making muffled noises as if he were trying to speak with a gag in his mouth, and I figured he'd been tied up also. We rocked back and forth as we were driven by the four cadets, and we tried to hear what they were saying to get a clue about what we were in for. It was a warm night and I was sweating and scared.

The vehicle stopped after a short ride and I heard Rexford laughing as I was picked up and slung over somebody's shoulder. I was carried a short way and dropped hard on a carpeted floor. A nearby thud told me Fager had been dropped next to me. The burlap and blindfolds came off and we saw the four of them laughing as they left the room and locked the door behind them. Fager and I looked at each other and struggled helplessly, but we couldn't move or do much more than roll around on the floor. This isn't so bad, I thought, as I relaxed a bit. I figured this was the extent of the cadets' plans, to kidnap us and leave us tied up in a strange place. But it was obviously some sort of house so someone would find us if we didn't panic, so I tried to adjust to my surroundings.

Rexford, Hunt, McDermott and Nichols unlocked the door and stood over us. All four wore tight white muscle shirts and tight black pants and were barefoot. We were untied and ungagged and ordered to attention by Rexford, while the others lounged on chairs or the floor and drank Wild Turkey. Rexford went into drill instructor mode, barking orders and spitting in our faces, calling us every name in the book. At every accusation, we had to answer "YES SIR!" And then quietly, he said, "Take off your clothes." Neither one of us moved right away to unbutton anything, until he screamed "MOVE! GET FUCKING NAKED NOW! DID YOU HEAR ME?" Fager looked at me, scared, and we got naked and stood before Rexford and the others at attention as ordered. They laughed and continued to harangue us, tossing insults at our manhood and our naked bodies. But I didn't think we had anything to be ashamed of, and neither did they.

Rexford growled insults as McDermott and Nichols roped our hands behind our backs. I sneaked a look at Fager being tied and Rexford slapped me across the face, reminding me that I was at attention. We stood ramrod straight as duct tape was slapped across our eyes and mouths. I jumped when a hand prodded my balls and nipples. Rexford said, "The Faggot is first." I was pushed on the floor next to the bed with my head on something soft like a pillow, and someone tied my ankles together.

I could hear them toss Fager on the bed, followed by rustling of cloth and zippers. The bed springs creaked in a steady rhythm, and Fager was howling until McDermott told him to shut up. Rexford said he'd "open him up" with his "soldier." Fager was getting fucked, gang-fucked, I figured. I rolled off the pillow and rubbed my face against the rug on a loose spot of tape over my eyes. I wanted to get loose, but I wanted to witness Fager's rape. It was like an accident on the freeway, you had to look. I burned my face rubbing the rug, but I got the tape off one eye and carefully turned toward the bed so they wouldn't notice. I could just see Nichols on top of Fager, his crotch against Fager's ass and driving up and down. Rexford and McDermott were naked and watching assiduously, fingering their cocks and each other. I couldn't see Hunt but I could hear his non-stop dirty talk urging Nichols on. Fager had quieted down, moaning softly only when a new cock went up his ass.

Then it was my turn. Fager's and my positions were reversed, him on the floor, me on the bed, and my feet were untied and spread. "I don't want him crawling away. Tie his feet," Rexford said. I couldn't see pressed against the bed, but I assume Fager's ankles were bound. "My turn," McDermott said, and he spit in my ass and raped me fast. I've never felt so helpless before or since, but there was an undeniable thrill and I hated the fact that I was enjoying some of this. Does that make sense? I suppose the advantage to being fucked second was that the four of them had already warmed up on Fager, so they came quickly when they fucked me. I could feel a damp spot on the bed, where Fager had cum I assumed. Rexford said "antiwar Commie freaks" deserved to be treated like fuckin' cracks and worse. Fager was moaning loudly, as if they were molesting him or something on the floor, but again I couldn't see from where I was.

I think Hunt fucked me last, and he was the roughest. I could feel their cum in my ass oozing around. A minute later, they put Fager on the bed next to me. I knew it was him because I felt the ropes and heard him groaning. We were told, ordered, not to report this because no one would help us and we'd get raped again, and harder, if anyone was told. Fager and I had both cum, and Rexford said that meant we enjoyed it, and wouldn't our parents love to hear that? They got dressed and left.

I don't know how long it took, but Fager made progress against the ropes until I heard him pull the tape off his face and breathe hard. His hand on my butt was the first hopeful thing I'd known in hours. He took off the tape on my face and untied me. We just lay on the bed for awhile and stared at each other. What do you say when you've just been raped? But we knew we weren't telling anyone, until now that is, long after the fact. We looked for our clothes but they'd taken or hidden everything except our underwear and socks. It was good that we didn't have far to walk. Turned out we were in a house on the Academy property that was used as a faculty guest house, and thank God it was empty so no one saw us half naked and looking like shit. We walked for almost a mile back to the dormitory, feeling crappy and degraded.

Rexford and the others never said anything about it because we kept quiet. It freaked out Fager for a day or so, just as Capwell and Nuell had been sorely intimidated. But we all treated Rexford with renewed respect. He was still wrong about Vietnam, but we spoke with only a small portion of our minds around him.

Are we not men?

ONE
OF THE BOYS

I was never a frat rat, but I got initiated into a high school circle and it was an all day strip naked bondage experience. It happened when I was sixteen years old, back in '84. There was a bunch of hot looking guys who hung out together, known at school as the Boys Club or just the Boys. They usually wore white T shirts, blue jeans and sneakers without socks like a uniform, and they looked fucking hot. It wasn't just the look. It was the attitude. Not dangerous, just cool and assured, and I wanted in the Club. Brian was my best friend and jackoff companion, and he'd been initiated as one of the Boys early that year. The initiation was supposed to be a secret, but Brian told me he'd been tied up a lot and forced to crawl around naked. Now I really wanted in, and I stopped just short of selling myself into slavery to get on their good side, until Brian and club prez Gary invited me to join.

For the initiation, I came to the park behind the high school at 6:30 in the morning on Saturday, as instructed. Gary ordered, that's right, ordered me to wear the Boys' uniform of clean white T shirt, old jeans and sneakers without socks. Precisely at 7, the big LTD that belonged to Gary's mother pulled up near me, and six of the Boys approached me, all wearing the same outfits. Two of the Boys, Harlan and Ed, pinned my arms while Gary shoved his snotrag in my mouth. They pushed me down on the wet grass and had me naked as sin in seconds, and I couldn't fight them cause they held me down. My hands, feet and knees were tied up. I couldn't scream since Brian tied a white sweatsock around my mouth. A pillowcase went over my head, and they stuffed me in the trunk of the car and we drove off. God, I was terrified. I felt like the biggest dork in the world, letting myself get literally roped into this.

The Boys' clubhouse was a large cabin out near the lake, a half hour drive out of town. Gary's parents owned it, and I guess they didn't care if he used it, or for what. They carried me in and dumped me on the rug, and removed the pillowcase, jerking me by the hair and molesting parts of me that had never been molested before. I was panting and red faced, and nervous because I was naked.

The initiation proper kicked off as I was shoved into a wooden chair and tied into it, immobile and fucking helpless. Gary told me I would spend the day as their prisoner to see if I could take torture like a man. As he spoke, he was hitting my thigh and dick with a stick for emphasis. My legs had been spread out and tied to the edges of the chair, so I was vulnerable. Every time I made a muffled plea, the others made fun of my attempts to yell for help, imitating my moans and making "Uummmmph! Nnnmmmph!" noises. They started pulling on my dick quite openly, yelling "Boner! Boner!" when I got hard. It was like that's what they wanted. A senior named Todd got off on pinching my nipples and pulling out my pubic hairs, just to hear me cry out, or try to.

They untied me and gave me 30 seconds to use the bathroom. Escape through the window would've meant a long, long naked run home.

The Boys stripped out of their clothes for a swim in the lake. Gary, Brian, Ed and Harlan swam naked. Todd and Griffin had the briefest of trunks that barely concealed their dicks and butts. Harlan stuck his hand over my mouth and forced me to the back porch. I was tied up, spreadeagled and standing up, with my wrists and feet spread and bound to the railings. I was gagged with the same spit-soaked handkerchief and sweatsock. I twisted and twisted to try and get free while they splashed around in the lake. This was my chance to escape, grab somebody's clothes and the car keys and split. But I looked up at one bound hand and then the other and I gave up, deciding instead to take my bondage torture without flinching. Or at least not much flinching. I had to prove myself to these guys.

The Boys returned, and I was still hanging around. Todd pulled out his dick and shook it at me, and I got stiff again. I got stiffer when the Boys took paddles and some coffee table sized books and pounded my ass good and hard.

I was untied but still gagged, and I was sent to the kitchen to prepare sandwiches and beer while the Boys put on jeans or shorts. I don't think anybody put on a shirt the rest of the day. Brian came in to do a gag check, wearing cutoffs so short they were practically underwear. I was so distracted by his body that I nearly whacked off my finger with a knife, and Brian smiled at the effect this was having on me.

Lunch was served, and I was the main course. Todd and Harlan tied me stretched and spread-eagled to the table, on my back. I was still stuffed with the spitty gag, and had nothing to say. The Boys roped me tight to the four corners, and gathered round to smoke cigs and eat the food I made. Ed had his feet on the table, practically in my face. He'd push the sole of his foot against my cheek and laugh. Brian and Griffin each sat with a leg slung over the side of their chairs, stretching and scratching their crotches at me. And Harlan was lighting matches and holding them to the bottom of my feet, and he tried to singe the peach fuzz on my legs. I jerked and twisted at each assault, and the Boys got a kick out of my gagged screams.

Gary untied me and removed the gag, but he kept his hand over my mouth. The Boys had to have a secret meeting, so I had to disappear. They locked me in a bedroom, after tying me up and leaving some beer in a dog dish and a sandwich that I was to consume as best as possible. Jesus. I made the best of it, lapping up the beer and gnawing the food, and trying not to lose it completely. My fate in The Boys Club was being decided at that moment, I figured.

I probably fell asleep for a little while, but I woke to the sensation of hands slapping and squeezing my balls. I felt my ankles being untied, and as my senses were returning I was dragged to my feet and escorted to the living room. My two newest friends, the wet handkerchief and the sock, were used to gag me again. All six Boys stood around me in a circle. They started pushing me around back and forth from Boy to Boy, in a kind of circular gauntlet, screaming in my face while chanting the principles of the Boys' brotherhood. It got harder to steady myself as they slapped at my body, and I hit the floor surrounded by twelve ankles and sixty toes. Gary smiled at the others and removed my gag, while pulling down his pants. He told me to suck Boy cock if I wanted to be a Boy.

I was too tired to fight it, even if I'd foolishly wanted to, and I humbly accepted Gary's force fed dick. I crawled on my knees and one by one took each dick in my mouth, sucking them until everyone was hard and pointing at me in the circle. Some of the Boys were pulling on their own dicks and moaning hard. Harlan had a hand on Todd's ass.

Gary said it was time to be "poked" for being "a good little cocksucker." The Boys tied me to a leather couch, painfully prone on my hard dick. "These'll be in the way," Brian said, as he untied my hands behind my back. They were stretched before me and tied together to the couch. Gagged again, one ankle was tied down, and a Boy held my other foot, tickling it and spreading my legs wide. Split wide, I learned that a poke meant getting a Boy dick up the ass. Shouts of "fuck him, fuck him!" or "go-go-go" erupted as Gary, then Harlan, then Brian and the rest stuck their dicks up my hole in turn, some really fucking me and pumping, others rock steady riding me while I bucked and cried out underneath. Then they all took a breather and fucked me again. My neck and back were covered with sweat and slobber. There was a pecking order as far as who was next in line to "poke" me. Brian got a little too anxious, and tried to cut in line. A shoving match broke out, ending up with Brian being subdued, and bound and gagged himself! Brian and I both wrestled with our bondage while the others jacked off until their dicks dripped cum.

I was welcomed in as one of the Boys, they gave me back my clothes, but my smart mouth got me in trouble. They tied me up again, clothed but barefoot, and put me in the trunk for the drive home. Brian rode home gagged, with bound hands. Asshole behavior meant punishment, usually by bondage.

Others who came to the Boys after me got my warm, personal attention in their bondage initiation. And boy, did those boys get it. We had one Boy in bondage all night and most of the next day. Another one got strung up from a tree limb, with his ties a foot off the ground, and we all pissed on the gagged sucker and left him to dry in the sun. And another one got tied and gagged and whipped with our belts until he was very nearly bleeding. But nobody complained much. We knew how to pick 'em.

YOUNG ROPERS

I grew up on a small farm in Minnesota during the sixties and early seventies as the only child of deeply religious parents who were pillars of the local Swedish Lutheran Church. Their philosophy of parenting is best illustrated by the well-used length of heavy cowhide which hung from a hook on the back porch, over which was tacked a little hand-lettered, cardboard sign reading: "HE WHO SPARES THE ROD HATES HIS SON. BUT HE WHO LOVES HIM IS CAREFUL TO DISCIPLINE HIM." — Proverbs 13:24. The one thing my father will *never* be accused of is sparing the rod.

As I was growing up, although my parents often punished me by grounding me, assigning me extra chores, washing out my mouth with soap, or sending me to my room without any supper, the one punishment I could always count on, in addition to all of the others, would be a trip to the utility shed for a whipping. To make it even worse, rather than taking me out there right away and punishing me on the spot, my father would often make me sweat out a whole day or more with the threat of a beating hanging over my head.

I was in the seventh grade when my father decided that I was old enough to graduate from over-the-knee-spankings in his bedroom to real, man-sized whippings in the shed. Since he had grown tired of my kicking and squirming and trying to protect my ass during spankings, he decided it would be better for me, as well as more manly, if I had no control over what was happening to me. Consequently, from then on, I was to be tied over a sawhorse for my whippings. To make the whole thing even worse, my father gave me the job of installing the leather harness straps on the legs of the sawhorse so that my wrists and ankles could be secured quickly and easily.

The ritual for my punishment sessions never varied very much. When the hour of reckoning finally arrived, I would have to go get the strap from the back porch and bring it to the shed where I would lay it over one end of the sawhorse. If the weather was real cold my next job would be to light the portable heater. Then I would have to go and stand with my face pressed into the one empty corner of the shed and think about what I had done wrong and about how much my ass was going to smart for it. I could always count on its being at least an hour before I would hear my father's heavy footsteps coming up the path. After entering and seating himself on a high wooden stool, he would order me to come over and stand in front of him. Then he would make me look him straight in the eye while he gave me a long lecture about what I had done to piss him off and just why it was that I needed this whipping. After this came the really humiliating part. He would make me take off all my clothes before bending me over the sawhorse. Then I had to spreadeagle my arms and legs so they could be tied with the leather straps to the legs of the horse.

As soon as I was secured over the horse, my father would pick up the strap and go to work on my ass. The blows would land hard and in rapid succession which caused a hell of a lot of pain to build up in a hurry and was aggravated by the fact that he kept all his licks aimed only at my butt-cheeks. After our first couple sessions in the shed I actually began to believe my father was doing me a favor by tying me down. If I had to be whipped, being restrained was the only possible way I could have taken a thrashing this bad.

By the time I was in tenth grade this whole situation had become really embarrassing since none of my friends were still being whipped by their fathers. The one time I worked up enough courage to mention this to my father, I was told grimly that every one of them would still be getting the strap if he had anything to say about it.

During the late spring of my sophomore year in high school, my mother's brother offered my parents a way to get out from under the burden of our farm which was, by then, going steadily down the tubes. My uncle, who was rapidly becoming a very successful rancher in southwest Texas, offered my father a good job and a house to live in, He also put me to work as a hand full-time during the summer and part-time during the school year. Even though my father never whipped me again after we moved to Texas, my next experience with ass beating was to begin shortly. It happened when I decided to go out for Young Ropers, a rodeo club for young men ages sixteen up to twenty-one.

Our initiation took place over a weekend in mid-August when the entire group members, would-be members and spon-sors all saddled up their horses and rode off for a campout on property owned by the father of one of the club members. I learned later that this location was always chosen because of its God-forsaken remoteness. This was to guarantee that the club would be able to initiate its new members without any danger of being observed. Complete privacy was an important consid-eration given the kind of hazing the Ropers liked to do. Even though it only lasted forty-eight hours, it was the longest forty-eight hours I had ever experienced in my whole fucking life. In spite of all the participants being sworn to secrecy every year, the Ropers had a kind of ominous reputation which kept all but the toughest most macho boys from joining.

In addition to the eleven adult sponsors of the group, all of whom were former club members, we also had with us two honorary sponsors who had arranged to take the weekend off. One of these was the local Lutheran minister, a large, muscular, good-looking former college football jock in his late twenties who served as the club's chaplain. The other man was a doctor and the father of one of the club members. Feeling the need to bring a doctor along says volumes about Young Roper initiations.

In preparation for the weekend we had been forbidden to bring any clothing except what we would be wearing. We were told to wear hats, boots, leather work gloves and bandannas around our necks. Our jeans were to be Wranglers, which happened to be the "official" pants of the Ropers. We were not to bring any toiletries, not even razors or tooth brushes. We were to bring only a sleeping bag and a paper grocery sack with our name printed on it which was to contain a roll of toilet paper and six spring-loaded clothespins. We had also been ordered to show up at the meeting place Friday afternoon wearing quarter inch crew cuts. The worst part was that we had also been warned not to appear under any circumstances unless the rest of our bodies were completely hairless: even our armpits, cocks and balls. Any hair found on us would be pulled out with tweezers.

What made this so bad for me was that I had hair in places I couldn't reach. Finally, after giving the matter a lot of thought, I swallowed my pride and asked Garth, one of my best friends, if he would help me out. Garth, who was also being initiated into the Ropers said he had the same problem. This being the case, we decided to trade shaves. Even though both of us got hard as rocks while having our crotches shaved, we just laughed it off as something caused by the necessary handling and nothing more. You can bet your ass that all this shaving was done over at Garth's house and not mine. My father would have had a shit hemorrhage if he'd caught us in the act.

On Friday of that fateful weekend, after a two hour ride on horseback, we arrived at the campsite in the late afternoon and pitched the tents. Those of us being initiated were given a lecture by the club president which was carefully calculated to scare the shit out of us. He said that for the next two days we would be lowly jackasses without speech and with no rights. We were the sole property of the club members who could do with us as they damn well pleased. We would obey all commands instantly. Any disobedience, or sounds, other than whimpering when hurt, would be punished in a manner easily understood by any jackass: in other words, with a whip. The bottom line was that, for the remainder of the weekend, the eight of us would be totally at the mercy of two dozen young cowboys who, as we would soon discover, had a real talent for doing painful things with whips, paddles, hot shots and a few yards of rope.

After our situation had been explained to us, each jackass was assigned to his three "mule skinners" who were the club members who would have direct charge over him. I was remanded to the custody of Craig, Justin and Troy who would, later on, become three of my best friends. This would be an interesting transformation given the fact that, during that weekend, I had more than a little proof that they were all total assholes as well as my worst enemies.

The first thing the mule skinners did was to get the eight of us stripped naked. Except for our socks and boots, we wouldn't see our clothes again until late Sunday afternoon when we were getting ready to ride back to town. As soon as I had been relieved of my boots and socks, Justin started popping the buttons on my shirt while Craig ripped off my jeans. While those two guys were busy stuffing my clothes into my grocery sack, Troy ambled over and, grasping the leg bands of my cotton jockeys whispered, "Okay, big jack, it's time to see what these little white fuckers are hiding." As he slid my shorts down my legs I felt a tingling in my crotch and knew that I was getting hard. Since I had always thought of myself as super-straight, I was struggling with a lot of confusion as to just why the hell I was getting so fucking turned on having my underpants taken off by a goddam boy. What made it even worse was that Troy, instead of ignoring my problem, gave my stiffening cock a couple real hard squeezes and whistled "Goddam!" under his breath. Then he hollered, "Hey y'all! Come over here and take a gander at what this fuckin' donkey's got hangin' on him. We oughter hire 'im out for stud service! Let's get us a mare and we'll make us some goddam mules!"

As soon as my three mule skinners had me stripped, they got some rope and went to work positioning my arms so they could tie my hands and elbows behind my back, which was the way they would be kept except when I was to be tied in some other position. As Craig buckled a large studded dog collar around my neck he told me that all the jackasses would be wearing these collars day and night until after we had been formally initiated the following weekend. It was sort of embarrassing in that everybody in the whole damn town would want to know why we were wearing those big black and chrome collars.

By now it was supper time. We were made to eat all our meals kneeling on the ground with our hands still tied behind us. Anybody who has ever tried to eat this way knows how hard it is to keep from falling face-first into your dish. Our food consisted entirely of cold baked beans which had been laced with castor oil, the amount of which was designed to give us the runs for the entire weekend. An even worse torture was that, while we were eating this shit, we were forced to smell the food the members were cooking for themselves: grilled steaks, chicken and ribs, as well as potatoes and sweet corn which had been roasted in the coals of the fire.

As soon as supper was finished, all eight of us jackasses were strung up to overhead branches with our feet tied to stakes after they had been spread as far apart as our mule skinners could kick them. Another stake was pounded into the ground six or eight feet in front of us to which our cocks and balls were roped so tightly that there was always an uncomfortable tugging sensation. After we had been gagged with bits they blindfolded us with our own bandannas. The mule skinners then used our bodies to hone their whipping skills. In theory, the object of the exercise was to flick lightly whatever part of the anatomy was targeted. In reality, however, most of these guys weren't all that good with a whip, which left the eight of us pretty well striped and covered with welts. All in all, my ass was the part of me hardest hit. Because of all the whipping and paddling they put us through that weekend, I was still oozing small amounts of blood into my underwear three day later. In order to fight infection, the doc insisted that we have rubbing alcohol daubed into our wounds several times each day which also, of course, provided some pretty good torture all by itself.

We were made to spend our nights naked, imprisoned inside our zipped-up sleeping bags with our ankles and knees tied and our wrists bound behind our backs. In addition to all the other painful crap being done to us, we also had to put up with the cramping caused by the castor oil which was constantly tearing up our guts. We were only allowed to dump just before bedtime, so any boy who couldn't hold his shit until reveille had no other choice but to go in his sleeping bag and sleep with both it and the stench for the rest of the weekend.

Saturday morning, after chowing down on more cold beans and somewhat less castor oil, our mule skinners freed our hands and put us through an hour or so of PT: endless push-ups, jumping-jacks, leg-lifts and sit-ups. By now the day was getting hotter than hell so we were given a short break for water, having been told by the doctor to drink plenty of it.

As soon as we had drunk our fill, we were allowed to have some sunscreen, especially for those less exposed areas below the belt, but with the stipulation that we were not to rub it on ourselves. Since the doc had warned us not to overlook our gonads, all eight of us found ourselves in the embarrassing position of being forced to handle each other's cock and balls. We were deluged with raucous catcalls and laughter when the mule skinners discovered that most of us had sprouted hard-ons as the result of having our cocks massaged by our partner's oily hands. This, of course, gave some asshole the brilliant idea that each boy should keep yanking on his buddy's pecker until he came. My brain was flooded with mixed feelings as my partner who, luckily, was Garth, went to work jacking me off in front of the jeering crowd.

In spite of all the good feelings Garth's hands were giving me as he milked my shaft, I was also fighting a lot of guilt and embarrassment. The guilt came mostly from the fact that it hadn't been all that long since my father had last whipped my ass for jerking off. I remembered all too well that day when, just before moving to Texas, my father had caught me soaking in a hot bathtub with my cock in my fist. Now, at this point, I was having real uneasy thoughts about what might happen if my father ever happened to hear about what Garth and I had done to each other. I was pretty sure that he would probably start whipping me again and it wouldn't matter a rat's ass that I had been given no choice in the matter.

At least some of the embarrassment I was feeling was caused by having my minister see what Garth and I were doing with each other's penises. I do remember being kind of surprised that neither the doc nor Pastor Petersen took any steps to stop the action. Our pastor back in Minnesota had been very prissy and uptight and would have had a stroke had he seen what we were doing to each other. It was on that weekend that I learned just how callused and tough Texas men and boys can be; even ministers, most of whom I had always thought were sort of sissy.

After our cocks had been pumped dry, it was time for the donkey races. This time when the bits were fastened in our mouths they had short leather reins attached to them. No sooner had we been made to crouch on all fours at the starting line with a mule skinner mounted on our backs than the gun went off starting the stampede for the finish line. The total distance was probably no more than one-tenth of a mile, although at the time it seemed more like ten miles. This was because, in addition to having a heavy load on our backs, each of us was being tailed by what was called a "wand wizard," which, in reality, was just a goddam mule skinner brandishing a hot shot. Even though the voltage was much lower than what would be used on thick-skinned livestock, the jolts could still light up your eyeballs. Most of the zaps Troy hit me with were aimed directly at my asshole although, periodically, he would stoop over so he could blast me right in the balls. Not very many boys got to the finish line without tears in their eyes and a few had emptied their bowels along the way, due no doubt to a lethal combination of laxatives and electricity. If it hadn't been for our leather work gloves and the knee pads we'd been issued, there would have been no skin left on our hands and knees.

As soon as I collapsed over the finish line I knew what was in store for us when I saw all the mule skinners skimming off their wide leather belts. In less than a minute all of us except the winner were crawling through a forest of booted legs having our bare asses whipped good.

As soon as lunch was finished, the members saddled their horses for a game called "Chase the Horsy" in which each initiate is tethered on a rope behind a horse for a two mile run. To add a little spice, another mounted rider follows alongside swinging at the victim's backside with a large paddle. My hands were untied just long enough for me to go put on my socks and boots after which I was quickly surrounded by my three mule skinners who went to work on me with a vengeance. After putting the bit back in my mouth they took a long coil of rope, bound my wrists tightly together in front of me and tied the other end to the saddle of Justin's horse.

The worst part came when they started rubbing Ben Gay

into my cock, balls, buttocks and even up my asshole. Since I am uncircumcised, they seemed to take special pleasure in sliding back my foreskin and rubbing the fire grease around what would normally be the underneath side. After sliding my prepuce back over the head they decided to clip a couple of clothes pins to the loose skin. As an afterthought, Craig picked up a smooth stone, wrapped it with rope, and tied the other end to my ball sac so it would dangle just above my knees. Justin then allowed as how, since that looked "so fuckin' purty," maybe they ought to tie another rope around my cock and balls and fasten it to the saddle, too. It didn't take me very long to figure out that I would either keep up with the gait of the horse, or I would find myself being dragged behind it by my hands and balls. Just before mounting up, Troy and all the other members who would be riding shotgun, went and picked up their paddles.

The paddles they used on us that weekend were of unfinished wood and had obviously been cut from the same pattern. Since they were intended to be wielded occasionally while on horse-back, these boards were somewhat longer than the average fraternity paddle. They were probably a little over three feet in length, four inches wide, and close to an inch thick. Their size and weight, in addition to the fact that they also had some sizable holes drilled through them, meant that these hummers could pack one hell of a wallop, especially if gripped with both hands. When fired off under enough cowboy power, these boards would really explode on your tail raising blue welts on your ass wherever your hide came through the holes. If you got paddled long enough and hard enough, you would most likely end up with welts stacked on top of welts.

As soon as all the preparations had been made, everybody

got into traveling formation. Each of the eight groups consisted of the lead horse and rider followed by the poor jackass tethered to it on the end of a rope. On his left was the man riding shotgun, but armed with his paddle instead of a rifle. The sponsors and the mule skinners not directly involved were also mounted and were scattered around on both sides of the line. For a sixteen year old, even though I was a pretty big boy, it was still fucking intimidating to be standing on foot, naked and tied to the back of a horse, surrounded by so many mounted men. What made it even more awesome was that these dudes were muscular and powerfully built and most of them were stripped to the waist wearing only boots, hats, gloves and Wranglers. Even though I was scared shitless, I couldn't help noticing that even Pastor Petersen had shed his shirt and was showing off a washboard torso which out-rippled most of the other men in the party.

When the starting signal was given I was careful to keep my eye on Jason's horse in front of me. I probably began moving even before it did. Even though I was able to keep up with the gait Jason was setting, Troy seemed to enjoy seeing how many wallops he could land on my bare ass with his paddle. By the time we had reached the end of the line, all eight of us jackasses were still on our feet although, to a man, we had bright red asses. Even though I had tried to run bowlegged, I still had some bruises on my legs where the stone hanging from my balls had banged against them.

As soon as we had been untied from the horses we were told it was now rest time. I assumed we were going to be allowed to crash on the ground for a siesta. Instead, the eight of us were taken over to a triple split rail fence. After being relieved of our socks and boots, our mule skinners tied our forearms horizontally behind our backs and attached the end of the rope to the D-rings in our collars hoisting our arms high up on our backs. After blindfolding us with our bandannas and rubbing a fresh coating of Ben Gay into our asscracks, our mule skinners picked us up bodily and heaved us astride the fence making certain that the cracks of our asses were perfectly aligned and shoved down into the ridge on the top of the diamond-shaped rail. Then they placed our ankles, one over the other and bound them together under the middle rail. Since there was no way we could push up with our feet, our already sore asses had to bear the full weight of our bodies. As though this would not have caused me enough misery, my mule skinners had rubbed Ben Gay into my nipples and had fastened clothespins to them. It was a miserable couple of hours. In spite of our gags and our heroic efforts to act like men, an occasional whimper would be heard from some suffering jackass. Absolutely no mercy was shown by the mule skinners and, by the time we were taken down from the fence, our blindfolds were pretty well soaked with tears and sweat.

After this ordeal I could hardly stand upright and my biggest fear was that the mule skinners were going to run us back to camp tied behind the horses. Instead, we were marched back to camp chain-gang style, tied ankle to ankle, with a few feet of rope between each one of us; enough rope so that the guys on horseback could still get at us with their paddles. To allow easy access to our asses, our mule skinners had left our arms bound together and fastened to the rings in the backs of our dog collars.

At reveille early Sunday morning, each jackass was picked up bodily in his sleeping bag by his mule skinners and dumped out naked onto the ground. I knew I was in trouble when I saw that Craig, Justin and Troy already had their paddles with them. As soon as they had untied me, they grabbed my arms under my shoulders and dragged me off into a clump of trees where they could work me over in relative privacy. They allowed me barely enough time to piss and shit before putting me through my morning PT. Unlike the previous morning, I was put through my paces alone under the close supervision of my three tormentors who would paddle me most anytime my ass was exposed, especially while doing jumping-jacks and pushups.

As soon as breakfast was finished, the jackasses were forced to do the sunscreen and jerkoff routine again in front of the group. When we had drained each other, we were lined up and made to stand at attention while the members prepared us for the next activity. Having been given knee pads and gloves, twelve foot lengths of rope were then tied to the rings in our collars. After we had once again been gagged with bits, we were led out to where a wagon wheel had been attached horizontally to the top of a five foot fence post sunk upright in the ground. When our ropes had been fastened to the wheel the eight of us were ordered down on all fours. Then we were straddled by the club members, now stripped to the waist, who rode us around in circles like ponies in a carousel while they whipped our naked flanks with riding crops, belts or pieces of leather rein.

When the mule skinners finally tired of riding us they took a short break to get their paddles. Then they ordered us up off our knees and we were made to continue going around in circles, this time on our hands and feet with our bodies arched in the air. This, of course, made our asses perfect targets for the paddles. Whenever one of us collapsed from exhaustion, causing the carousel to grind to a halt, some asshole was always on hand to beat our butts continuously until we resumed our painful crawl.

By midmorning our black and blue asses made it obvious that none of us would be able to sit comfortably again for a long time. It was at this time that we were forced to sit for an hour while Pastor Petersen conducted our own church service. Just before the service began, in one hundred degree heat, we jackasses were issued woolen army blankets and ordered to cover our nakedness. In my case, the scratchy blanket rubbing against my sweaty, scratched and bruised body was a torture all by itself; an even bigger torture than church usually was.

I remember thinking, as I sat there fidgeting on my well-beaten butt, with every bone in my body aching, what irony it was to be listening to a sermon about the precious joys of brotherhood, and of the fellowship we were privileged to share as young men in the company of each other. As my pastor compared our companionship as Young Ropers to that of Christ and his disciples, I wondered grimly if the disciples had also been beaten black and blue before being allowed to join The Twelve. Somehow, I couldn't quite picture it. As I think back on it now, this was probably the only sermon I ever heard Pastor Petersen preach which was pure bullshit. The only good news was that we were able to rest for an hour and have our hands untied which felt real good.

While the sermon droned on, I looked at Derek. Derek was, hands down, the best looking stud being initiated. He was eighteen years old, fresh out of high school, and had just gotten married in May. Not only that, but his wife was already pregnant with their first child. Derek was tall and well-built, with fairly massive shoulders which tapered down to a slender waist and a nice, round ass. He was equipped with a thick, beautifully formed circumsized penis which hung down at least six inches when soft. Derek had dark wavy hair and the kind of sexy blue eyes which melted the heart of every girl in the high school.

As Pastor Petersen babbled on and on, I remember wondering what it must be like for Derek to have to submit to having another man's hand on his penis. The club members had taken Derek's wedding ring away from him before we had even left town and now, for some reason, they seemed to be giving him even more shit than they were giving the rest of us. Derek's personal mule skinners, who were among the oldest of the Ropers, really seemed to have it in for him. For one thing, they were forever rubbing Ben Gay on his cock and balls and up his asscrack even when the rest of us weren't getting it. They had also taken a razor and shaved Derek's head as bald as a billiard ball. In addition, it was obvious to me, at least, that they were giving Derek an awful lot of extra paddling. There were several times that weekend when they even made him bend over and grab his ankles in front of the group while one or more of them put the wood to his ass.

I also could not help noticing that Derek's mule skinners, equipped with their flashlights and paddles, had taken him off alone each night while the rest of us were being zipped into our sleeping bags. As they led him away, his hands would be tied behind his back and I could see that he had been gagged and blindfolded as well. From the redness and puffiness around his eyes each morning, I was pretty sure that he had been crying. I also couldn't help noticing at PT time Saturday morning, that Derek's mule skinners had wrapped a lot of coarse rope around the top of his ball sac, distending it and making his nuts look like two red plums.

Several months later, Garth, who had been in Derek's wedding, told me what he had learned about what had been done to Derek during those midnight sessions. Among other things, Derek had been kept tied up, paddled, and had been made to suck his mule skinners' cocks.

As soon as the boring service ended all hell broke loose again. The next activity on the schedule was a rodeo in which the mule skinners were the contestants and we were the livestock. We were taken, one at a time, and chased frantically around a pen until finally, exhausted, we would feel the lasso tighten around our chests. As the rider dismounted, the horse, which had been trained to back up by itself, would keep the rope taut against our chests until the rider could throw us to the ground. In normal calf roping, after the contestant has thrown the calf to the ground he ties three of its legs together. However, with us, the second we bit the dust we found ourselves being hogtied, both wrists tied to both ankles behind our backs. Having been tightly trussed we would be half carried, half dragged to the sidelines where we had to lie helplessly until all eight of us had been roped and tied.

After lunch, the jackasses were once again subjected to the indignity of being bound for a run behind the horses. This time we were driven a mile or so out to a sunbaked patch of clay where the eight of us were staked out, spreadeagled, in a circle around a big anthill. I couldn't believe this was actually happening to me. I felt as though I was some fucking settler who had been captured by the Indians as the mule skinners drizzled a thick sticky substance from the anthill over between our legs, up our groins and all over our hairless cocks and balls. Luckily, however, instead of slitting our eyelids in traditional Indian style, forcing us to stare at the sun until our eyes were fried, we were mercifully blindfolded instead. Then we were left alone for what seemed forever to wait for those little varmints to trail their way up our gooey crotches. Although I did get bitten pretty bad, especially on my balls, the worst part of this stake-out torture was psychological more than physical. Before the Ropers and their sponsors rode away leaving us to our fate, they told us they were going off to have a meeting to decide which of us had passed the test and were worthy to become club members.

At last, after what I guessed was about three hours, we heard the horses approaching and were finally untied from the stakes. Instead of making us hoof it back on foot we were tossed still blindfolded over the backs of horses with a rope connecting our wrists to our feet and hauled, corpse-style back to camp where we were literally tossed into a tank of water and told to clean ourselves up. I don't remember a bath ever feeling so fucking good!

As soon as we climbed out of the water we were made to line up and stand at attention to dry in the sun while the Roper president continued to fuck with our minds. He told us that it was the decision of the members that some of us had definitely proved our manhood more successfully that others, and that this had been a very difficult decision for the members to make. After playing cat and mouse with us for about five minutes, he pulled a list out of his shirt pocket and announced that he was going to read the names of the men who had been voted into Young Ropers.

I started counting on my fingers as he slowly read off the names. I was real happy, of course, when he read my name, but I was just as tickled a second later when I realized that he had read all eight names. Eight happier boys would be hard to imagine, and we quickly found ourselves hugging each other and dancing around wildly in circles. After we had calmed down, the president gave us our instructions for the coming week. We were also issued two bright red Roper T-shirts apiece, one of which we were to wear every day along with our dog collars until we were formally sworn into the club the next Friday night in the basement of the Lutheran Church.

After our clothes had been returned to us we saddled our horses for the ride back to town. I can't remember my clothes ever feeling so restrictive or uncomfortable as they did that day. The eight of us were battered, sore and mentally exhausted. But you can bet your sweet ass that this didn't keep any of us from feeling real proud that we had proved ourselves men enough to be voted into the Young Ropers Club.

The Ropers played an important part in my life for the next couple years until I graduated from high school and went into the Marines. Having lived a pretty isolated life on our farm in Minnesota, I hadn't realized just how much I had craved the company of other young men my age. Up to that point in my life, I had always been slow to make friends and develop relationships with people, even when I wanted to. As hellish as the Roper initiation was, the hazing I got that weekend was a real milestone in my growth and development because it forced me to get nose to nose with those men in a hurry. It was also in Young Ropers that I learned about the almost mystical bond which develops between men who find themselves giving and receiving pain in a dominant/submissive relationship.

JOINING THE FRAT

WEEPS
& ASSWIPES

As a college student in the early 1970's I joined a fraternity. It was considered a real macho/jock house. The pledge program was very physical. The point was to make things rough enough to weed out the "weeps and asswipes," as they were called. In the four years I was an active, at least three or four pledges dropped out of every class because they couldn't take the hazing the pledge masters dished out.

One of the house's hazing traditions was "games night." It always followed the same format and was a very popular event with the actives. A keg of beer was provided to get the audience up for the evening. The pledges were ordered to appear at the house at a particular time wearing only gym shorts, a jock and sneakers. They were lead into the basement by the pledge master who ordered them into formation while an audience of actives booed, whistled and made insulting remarks about their bodies, etc. The pledges were treated to a few minutes of PT to work up a sweat. The heat had been turned on fullblast and the room was like a steam bath. According to the "script," the pledge master would ask one of the pledges why he was sweating and he would dumbly reply because it was hot. The pledge master would get all "sympathetic" and then order the pledges to strip off their shorts and toss them into the audience. Smiling, he said that if the pledges were lucky they might get them back so they wouldn't have to walk back to their dorms bare-assed.

The pledges were run through a number of games in the course of the evening designed to exhaust, humiliate and/or nauseate them. One of the most entertaining was a variation of the grade school game dodge ball. The actives were armed with medium sized playground balls to throw at the pledges. When a pledge was hit, he was made to do pushups until the game was over. So the longer he could stay in the game, the less pushups he had to do. Of course the actives aimed for a pledge's cock and balls, hoping to inflict as much pain as possible. So when the first barrage of balls was let loose, the pledges covered their groins for protection. The pledge master would then blow a whistle and call a halt to the game.

He'd call the pledges weeps and pussies for trying to avoid a little pain in the cock and balls. He'd say they needed toughening up. He'd say that a [name of frat] needed to have iron balls. Then he'd bring out a number of short lengths of rope and with the help of some of the audience, each pledge's hands were tied behind him.

Once that was done, he and the assistant pledge master would take a magic marker and draw an arrow on each man's chest pointing down to his groin, saying that would give the audience something to aim for. The pledges were told they could move only left or right to avoid being hit. The game would resume. When just two or three players were left the pledge master would stop the game and blindfold the men to make them easier targets. The game might be played over three or four times before the actives got bored and a new game was introduced.

Also, in our house, if a pledge was particularly hairy and a fuck-up, he would be told to strip down to his shorts and sit in a chair. Then he would be "tied" to the chair with wide adhesive tape and set in the front hall on display. Of course, the tape came off eventually—usually with a good deal of the pledge's body hair.

PAINTED
PLEDGES

In 1983, I pledged a college fraternity my first semester at the state university. The fraternity (which I'll call Sigma Delta) was considered one of the two top frats on campus, filled with jocks and good looking, affluent young men. I was very lucky to get a bid, and I would have done almost anything to get through my pledgeship and be initiated as a brother.

Our pledgeship was mostly routine. In addition to memorizing lists of brothers' names and badge numbers, fraternity history and various oaths, we kept the frat house clean and served dinner. Though there was never any talk about hazing, we couldn't help but notice that standing in a corner of the basement party room was a huge, wooden chair nicknamed the "pledge throne." Nobody ever sat or talked about this massive piece of furniture, but both the name and the abundance of ring bolts sunk into the frame gave us something to worry about.

Hell Week marked the end of the pledgeship, and providing our first semester grades were good and we made it through Hell Week, we would become full fledged Sigma Delts. The first night of Hell Week was a Friday, and we were told to show up at the frat house at 10:00 p.m. wearing the following uniform: gym shorts & underwear, sneakers, a white tee shirt and a tie. Well, of course we looked ridiculous walking across campus in that silly costume, but all the pledges (about twenty of us) showed up at the frat house at 10.

We were told to gather and relax in the upstairs lounge where there was a keg of beer on tap. When we were needed someone would come and get us. We waited there and each had a beer or two, wondering what was going to happen to us. Finally at 11:00 p.m. Buck, the pledgemaster, came up with a big cardboard box filled with medium-sized grocery bags and a couple of pens.

"Listen up, pledges," Buck called out. "Each of you take one paper bag and write your name on it. Then take off sneakers, socks, gym shorts and tee shirts and put them in the bag. Then pile the bags in the corner. I want to see every one of you lined up outside in the hallway in 2 minutes wearing only underwear and a tie... Get moving!"

He stepped out into the hallway looking at his watch, and the room exploded into activity. Since there were only a couple of pens, everyone was grabbing at bags and scrambling to write their names while throwing clothes right and left. We ran out in the hallway and lined up according to height (I'm 5'11", so I was near the front) in just under two minutes. Then another couple of brothers joined Buck in the hallway and inspected us. They told us to throw out our chests, suck in our stomachs, etc. Buck walked up to a blond pledge named Steve, and pointed at a small, worn hole along the side of Steve's underwear.

"These are pathetic," Buck yelled. "What do you have to say for yourself?"

"Sorry, Sir," was Steve's excuse, which even I thought sounded sort of lame.

"Don't worry about it, pledge," Buck said soothingly. He then put two fingers inside the small hole and jerked his hand to the side, tearing the underwear from the elastic waist to the leg. Another jerk and the underwear were left in tatters, hanging like rags from the waistband and leaving Steve's ass and cock in full view.

Buck walked to the head of the line and stared up at Brian, who was the tallest pledge.

"Take your necktie off, Brian, and hand it to the pledge behind you." Brian did what he was told.

Buck then instructed the pledge to wrap the tie tightly around Brian's head and tie it in the back to act as a blindfold. After Brian was blindfolded, the third guy in line blindfolded the second, and on it went down the line until we all were tightly blindfolded. Buck then had us put our hands on the shoulder of the pledge in front of us and led us downstairs.

I could tell by the feel of the flooring under my bare feet that we were in the long hallway downstairs that led to the party room. The party room was a big room in the basement with a tile floor and a d.j. booth where we could throw parties and clean up easily afterwards. Now it sounded like the doors were closed and the room was filled with all the brothers, who were yelling things like, "Bring in the first victim," and "haul in more freshmen meat."

There was some whispering between Buck and the other two guys who were keeping an eye on us, then a knock on the big wooden doors, and then everything got quiet in the party room. I was extremely nervous, but also turned on, and I kept hoping that I wouldn't get some sort of embarrassing erection. Finally eerie music began to play on the other side of the doors, and I could hear Brian, the first pledge in line, utter a surprised "Hey!"

Buck quickly said, "Shut up, pledge. Come with us."

I could hear people moving, and the doors open and close. Obviously they had taken Brian inside, but that was all we could tell.

There was a lot of excited yelling and laughing coming through the door for the next five minutes, but it was too muffled to understand. Finally things quieted down and the doors opened again and the next pledge was led inside. This continued until they led the guy in front of me into the room, and I knew that I was next. By this time I had gotten really nervous, and I remember trembling a little, both from anxiety and from the cold tile floor under my bare feet.

The doors opened again and two brothers grabbed me firmly, one at each arm. They led me into the big party room, which I could tell was dark by the light filtering through the blindfold. The doors closed behind me, and I knew there was no turning back. I felt a third pair of hands touch me, grabbing the waistband of my underwear, surprisingly, and pulling them down around my ankles.

"Step out of these, pledge."

I stepped out of the underpants and was led to the massive pledge throne, which was what I had suspected all the while. Once seated, about four brothers scrambled around me, fastening me tightly to the chair with what felt like cotton rope. In less than a minute, my ankles were tied to the chair legs, my wrists were tied to the chair's sturdy arms, and a rope crisscrossed my chest. What made me feel the most helpless was that my knees were tied wide apart so I couldn't bring them together and protect my naked crotch. Though I am tall and lean, I have always had a large cock, and I could hear somebody comment about it in the back of the room, which made me feel even more self-conscious and embarrassed.

Once I was helplessly tied down, Buck said, "Alright, let's interrogate him. If you get any of these questions wrong, pledge, you are going to be sorry." This really made me nervous.

Questions began to be fired at me. "What is Brother Smith's pin number?" "Where was Sigma Delta founded?" " In what year?" "Who founded this chapter?" I answered them as quickly as possible, and having studied hard, only got a couple of questions wrong. Each time I answered wrong somebody would throw an egg or a water balloon, but because they had all been drinking, their aim was abysmal. The egg glanced off my shoulder and exploded against the chair back, and the water balloon exploded squarely on my left knee.

The interrogation lasted about two minutes, then Buck said, "This pledge has passed the test. Let's paint him!"

Within seconds, a crowd of guys were shoving around me, smelling strongly of beer. I could feel a half dozen wet paint brushes touch me all over, but I couldn't see what was going on. Someone was writing something across my chest, someone else was writing on my thighs, and strangest of all, about three paint brushes were concentrating on my genitals. First, paint was being slathered around the base of my cock, coating my pubic hair and the area surrounding my penis with paint. Astonishingly, someone even grabbed my penis and lifted it up, while another brush tickled and stroked my balls. Well, of course I became turned on immediately and became semi-erect. I covered it up as well as I could by laughing and yelling out, "Hey, cut it out, I'm ticklish!" Everyone was laughing and shoving around me, and no one seemed to care if I was ticklish, or erect, or anything other than a captive human canvas.

Next, paint brushes stroked the shaft of my penis from the point just behind the head to the base of the cock. Again, someone lifted my semi-hard penis up against my belly to paint underneath, which has always been incredibly sensitive. I squirmed and tried to close my legs but couldn't get away. Finally, a single brush twirled around the head of my penis. The brush was so wet and soft, and my penis was so sensitive, that I actually cried out, making everyone burst into laughter.

"O.K., this one is finished, put him in the corral."

They untied the ropes and I was pulled to my feet, dripping paint. I was led to a corner of the room when someone pulled my hands behind me and quickly tied them together. Then, Buck pulled off my blindfold. What I saw in front of me was incredible! Brian and the three other pledges brought ahead of me were all standing squashed together, hands tied behind them, with a single long rope thrown around all their chests like a lasso. They all had their future badge numbers painted across their chests in bright, neon poster paint. On their upper arms and thighs were written things like "property of Sigma Delt," "frat slave," etc. Incredibly, each of their penises were painted like a bullseye, with concentric red, yellow and blue rings. Above each piece of bizarre genital artwork was a slogan like "Use This Wisely," "Pencil Dick," or "Community Property." I looked down and, sure enough, I was painted exactly the same, with a bright neon penis and "Monster Dick" written on my belly. Before I could really get a look at this handiwork, the big lasso was lifted and I was pushed in with the other naked pledges. The rope circled us again and we were all pulled together tightly. "You're all brothers now," was Buck's comment, "so, you shouldn't mind this."

Since I was no longer blindfolded, I could watch and enjoy the next hour as they did the same to the last fifteen or so pledges.

By the time they got to the last guy, a short boy named Darryn, the corral took up the entire corner of the room and was a mass of naked freshmen. Buck said, "these guys are a mess, lets clean them up!" I knew what was about to happen…

The party room had big drains on the tile floor, and spigots in the nearby pantry to hook up heavy duty water hoses so we could easily clean up the place after an all-night beer party. Now the brothers turned those hoses on us, dousing us with cold water from all sides. The pledges yelled, squirmed and tried to hide from the hoses, but only got tangled up even more. I was near the middle, so I didn't get it too badly, but all the pushing and squirming, the bare feet slipping along the wet tiles, and the hands tied behind our backs led to the inevitable first pledge falling over. Luckily, when the first guy fell over, he took everyone else with him, and we all landed in a gigantic, naked, writhing mass of arms and legs, with no one hurt. The brothers must have taken some pity on us at this point, because they turned the taps over to warm water and kept dousing us for the next few minutes until we were all mostly clean. Then they turned the water off, threw the lights on and helped us to our feet. We were untied and led in groups of four to the showers, where we finished cleaning up. The rest of the evening was spent drinking beer and listening to the brothers tell us how silly we looked, but since it was all in good fun, and since no one was hurt or seriously humiliated, none of the pledges had any hard feelings.

The next night we were told to show up at the house at eight, in the same outfits of gym shorts, sneakers and white tee-shirts. We spent the evening cleaning the house up and doing chores, interspersed with occasional push-ups and question & answer sessions. We had to get every brother's signature on our pledge paddle that night, and in exchange for their signature, we had to allow them to take a swing at our butts with the paddle.

By midnight the frat house was spic and span, and we were told to gather in the dining room. Buck told us that the pledges would be broken up into pairs, and then hazed individually by a group of brothers. Everything seemed pretty well planned out, because groups of about four brothers would call out a pair of pledge names from a list.

I was paired up with a pledge named Todd, who happened to be a pal of mine from the dorm. What was interesting was that Todd was nearly exactly my height, had my swimmer's build, and had blondish hair like mine. We hung around a lot together, and some people thought we were brothers because we looked so much alike. We were given over to a group of four brothers who I knew were a clique in the fraternity, led by an overweight guy named Frank, who was frat treasurer. What I knew about these tight-knit guys was that they were all from Miami, they were all seniors and pretty influential in the frat. Todd and I walked over and waited by these four guys until all the groups were formed. Then the groups of brothers led their pledge pairs away. The vast majority of groups left the house entirely, heading out to various parts of campus. A couple of groups went out back of the house to where there was a big field. In the end, only a couple of groups remained in the house, of which we were one.

Frank led Todd, me, and the other brothers upstairs, where Frank's room was. In this wing of the frat house, all the rooms were two room suites with a sort of livingroom/bedroom and bath deal. We entered the livingroom part of the suite, and Frank locked the door. The four brothers went into the back bedroom and Frank said, just before he closed the connecting door, "we are going to be back in 5 minutes. I want you both standing at attention, facing the wall, entirely naked, with your clothes folded neatly on that chair when we open this door again."

The door closed again, and Todd and I looked at each other. I whispered, "do you think we should strip down to just our underwear? I don't know what they've got planned."

Todd looked at me and smiled sort of nervously. "Nah, we should do exactly what they said, because we don't want to screw up our chances of getting initiated tomorrow." Even as he spoke he was stripping out of his tee shirt and shoes "Here goes nothing," Todd continued, and skinned his gym shorts and underwear off. I did the same. We stood at attention, facing the wall, and waited until the guys opened the door again.

It seemed like a lot longer than 5 minutes before the door opened again. We were whispering to each other, saying how weird this was and how nervous we were, when the door opened up again and Frank said, "No talking, pledges." He told us to turn around, and I could see that Frank had some sort of hokey, crimson robe on with a hood. He tossed a wide, black bandana at Todd said, "blindfold pledge Nick, and make sure he can't see a thing." Todd did as he was told. Then, Frank led Todd and me into the bedroom. I couldn't see the other guys, but the little bit of light that filtered through the blindfold made me think the room was lighted with candles. Frank pushed me down into an armless, wooden chair and then told me to put my hands behind my back. I heard him tell Todd to kneel down and wait. Then, ropes were wrapped criss-cross around my wrists until they were secured together tightly. Other ropes were wrapped around each ankle, and then my feet were pulled back and tied to the top corners of the back chair legs, so that my toes couldn't touch the ground, and my knees were forced apart. With those few simple ropes, I was entirely helpless.

"This is your final initiation, pledge Nick. Listen carefully. I want you to recite the fraternity oath for us."

Well, this was easy. The fraternity oath was a sort of poem that consisted of about six sentences, which all the pledges had to know backwards and forwards. I quickly recited the oath.

"That was good. Now, I want you to continue reciting the oath, over and over, until I tell you to stop. I don't want to hear you hesitate or stutter even once. Your bid to become a brother is at stake... do you understand?"

"Yes, Sir!"

"One last thing," Frank continued with a sort of little laugh. "Todd, grab Nick's cock."

"What?" Todd exclaimed.

"Grab his penis!" Frank yelled. I felt a smooth, cool hand grasp my penis, which immediately became hard. "Now start jerking him off." Todd didn't ask any more questions but started to stroke my hardening cock as I began to squirm.

"Pledge Nick, start reciting the oath."

I began to repeat the frat oath, trying hard not to stutter or hesitate. It was nearly impossible! I didn't stutter, but I knew my voice was shaky, and I couldn't help but moan every once in a while.

"Louder!" Frank would yell at me. "Faster!" he would yell at Todd.

I kept up as best as I could, fumbling over words and getting more and more worried that I was screwing up my chances to become a brother. It seemed like an eternity as Todd vigorously pumped and pulled at my enormous erection and I kept yelling out the frat oath in a shaky voice. Finally, when I thought I couldn't take it any longer, another hand (not Todd's) reached down and firmly grabbed my balls, pulling them gently away from my body. Just as I began to feel the tide of my ejaculation rising, somebody else grabbed my hair and pulled my head back. I came as I yelled out the words from the oath, which no longer made sense to me.

"Okay, okay, that's enough." Frank finally said. "Todd, untie Nick and get a towel to clean him up." When that was all done. My blindfold was removed and I was told to blindfold Todd. His face was all flushed and he was panting a little, and his penis was so hard that it nearly slapped his belly even while standing. After he was blindfolded, and as he was being seated, I whispered to Todd, "your turn, big guy," and laughed. Now they told me to kneel beside him, and tied Todd securely to the chair the same way I was. Mark, the guy who must have pulled my head back in the end, must have liked the way that looked, because he looped a rope loosely around Todd's neck and tied it to the back of the chair, forcing his chest out. I was kneeling on the floor, and I couldn't keep my eyes off Todd's toes .

"Todd, start reciting the oath. The same rules apply. Nick, you know what to do."

I was determined to make Todd squirm even more than I did. I used one hand to encircle the base of his cock and grip it tightly, while I stroked the shaft and head of his penis with the other. The guys saw this and laughed, and Todd could hardly speak, much less recite the oath. "Stop stuttering, Pledge Todd," Frank yelled, and pinched both of Todd's nipples. Todd yelped and started to recite in what sounded like English. As Todd squirmed and stumbled through the oath, Frank twirled and pinched his nipples, and I kept pumping his erection. Within about 30 seconds, Todd was yelling and shooting all over his belly, high enough to hit his shoulder. "Oh, God, Stop! Stop!" Todd yelled. Everyone laughed and Frank gave me the order to stop. We cleaned Todd up and released him.

Neither Todd nor I, or any of the guys who were involved in that strange scene ever talked about it much, and from what the other pledges told me, none of them were involved in anything quite that kinky.

TOLERATED
BUT NOT HEARD

Theta pledges got themselves roped and ravaged throughout Hell Week. First of all, we had to strip naked in the front hallway, even if the door was still open. We were gagged and kept that way, because pledges should be tolerated but not heard. The gags were usually just clothes or handkerchiefs tied over our mouths, more for symbolic and visual effect than function. That way, our roles were defined and we were kept more or less quiet but we could still respond to commands or speak when we were spoken to. God help the pledge who complained or tried to remove the gag.

I did that and got gagged for real with a snotty handkerchief down my throat and a sock tied over it. My hands and feet were tied up and they left me on the floor in the middle of the lounge, where everyone could see me and brush or kick or just molest me to their heart's delight.

Pledges dined from dog dishes on the floor, on our knees with our hands tied. Meals were one of the few times we weren't gagged.

During Hell Week we didn't have our usual kitchen clean-up detail. We were gagged again and left tied up in what the actives called the Ready Room, while they prepared for the night's entertainment.

We were led to the room by an active with his hand gripping our dicks and balls like a leash.

We were stretched tight between two posts and our bodies were beaten with pledge paddles. Our asses got most of the attention, but groins, torsos and legs were easy prey, too.

After some more abuse, like being used as targets for streams of upperclassman urine or toy guns with suction cup arrows, pledges were blindfolded and got spanked or fucked or both, bent over somebody's bed. Feet were spread and tied to a footboard, and hands were stretched over our heads and tied to the bed post.

We slept in bondage, lived in bondage, and we did it to the pledges that followed us. It was the best thing about being in college. I'm sorry so many fraternities are wimping out on bondage and initiations today.

MY LIFE AS A DOG

When I was a freshman, I pledged into a great fraternity, and they kept me on a short leash. I was scared, I was turned on, and I was tied up. A lot!

My frat has a laid back but firm attitude about pledges in bondage: They deserve it, they're asking for it, and we're the men to do it. Rush was fairly informal, over some dinners at the house. When they asked me back for a second evening, I knew they were interested in me and vice versa. Five other interested froshes were there that night.

After dinner an upperclassman announced there would be a game. All the freshmen were pulled out of their seats and tied to posts, hand and feet. We were gagged so we could give the speaker our undivided attention. He gave us the sales pitch on Greek life and that frat in particular. I had always imagined what being tied up would be like, and I was thrilled. But I tried not to show it. A couple of other bondees wriggled uneasily and seemed put off but the rest of us got into it, as a joke at least. Being gagged and tied was much more satisfying than endless jock talk or the Billionaire Boys' Club stuffiness at some frats. The house president hinted that initiation "could mean more nights like this, all tied up." I pledged the second they asked me.

Initiation took place the week after midterms, but bondage-laden servitude started earlier. Sometimes, they would tie our hands at meals and we ate by bending forward with our faces in our food.

We had required chores, naturally, but on Saturdays and Sundays we had to shuck our shirts at the door and labor half naked. We pledges started calling ourselves The Skins. At first the upperclassmen were The Shirts, but somehow we decided to start calling them The Suits, at least when they were not around, as in The Guys In The Suits Who Are In Charge Of Everything. Sometimes we'd finish cleaning or painting and get tied up and gagged for the afternoon. We Skins were used as foot stools, pillows, beasts of burden or maybe Objets d'art, whatever the Suits wanted. Usually, we could untie ourselves pretty easily, since the Suits wouldn't, so it isn't as if it was so uncomfortable. But some of The Suits were better at knots than others. Even the ones who didn't do much tying up commanded respect and were called Sir. One Suit sat on me on the living room windowsill and calmly tied and gagged me as the other Suits watched. And then he squeezed the daylights out of my nipples. The pain. I thought I would cry or something. He looked at me and patted my cheek, and went away without saying anything the whole time. The Suits who were watching applauded and started teasing and pinching me. I decided to stay on that fellow's good side from then on. He'd made our roles clear without explanations or apologies.

After an evening studying at the library, a couple of Suits came with me back to my dorm. In my room, the visit became house business when the Suits ordered me out of most of my clothes and grabbed me. Before they left, I was wearing a pair of jams, face down and tied to the corners of the bed, gagged with my own socks, with three familiar Greek letters sketched on my naked back. I spent two hours trying to get loose. Boy, was my roommate surprised when he came home and had to untie me. All the Skins got a touch of bondage that night in their dorm rooms. Some didn't get untied till the wee small hours of the morning.

At a football game, the Skins, dressed for a change, had our wrists shackled and all chained together, resembling a prison work detail. Getting through the crowd in the stadium to our seats that way was a painful lesson in single mindedness of purpose. And when one guy did the Wave, we all did the Wave. When one guy went to the urinal, we all went to the urinal. Our team won the game, and the Suits declared that having us chained together was a good omen. We went to all remaining home games and one away game that way!

Initiation neared, and incidents of bondage and servitude increased. At least one Skin was tied up due to some violation of orders every day. Good natured joshing from the Suits became out and out abuse, but they could get away with it and we wanted to belong. Take the jockstrap rule, please. We had orders to wear jocks instead of regular underwear every day. The Suits staged unscheduled checkups, and if you didn't have your jock on, you were stripped naked and tied up.

Wednesday night. Rules of the Game. The Skins worked like slaves to get the house ready for the initiation rituals, just wearing our jockstraps. Then we were tied to posts and given orders. We were to stay in the House Thursday night through Monday morning, breaking that pattern for Friday classes if we couldn't skip them. A Skin protested, something about having a date, and we were all gagged tightly. We could bring one change of clothes to wear at classes on Friday and Monday, but no more. No underwear, no socks allowed. All other necessary clothing would be provided, the Suits said, and we had to wear our jocks. Each Skin received a new jock, plus a white t-shirt and white gym shorts. We were to show up on time, wearing that outfit and nothing else. No discussion, no exceptions.

Thursday night. The Dogs Do Bark. After dinner, the Suits made the Skins kneel before them. Each Skin got a dog collar fastened around his throat, and we all received our new dog names for the Initiation. One fellow was Fido. Another was Rover. The rest of us got names like Prince, Blackie, Benji, Astro, Brownie, Muttley, Tramp and yours truly, Rin Tin Tin, because I'm half German. I don't remember the other names. Blackie was not a racist slur, if you're curious. In fact, the only black fellow in the Skins and the best looking of all of us, a Roger Craig lookalike, got the name Prince. Blackie, ironically, was the palest white boy I'd ever met. We lay prone as our clothes, such as they were, were torn off of us, while everybody cheered and laughed at us in our jockstraps. Leashes were attached to the collars and we were pulled around on all fours, like pooches at the Westminster Kennel Club.

We were now dogs and had to act like dogs. That included barking instead of talking, begging, fetching, rolling over, whatever they wanted. The Suits whistled and slapped our vulnerable dog asses. We were fed dog biscuits, and made to piss in a big pan by raising one leg and aiming carefully. Some of the Suits climbed on our backs and took a horsie ride, or maybe a doggy ride, kicking and taunting us. They staged a race to see who could crawl fastest. The winner got a doggy treat, which he had to eat. The loser got a leather strap taken to his ass.

One of the dogs was caught standing on his hind legs, as if he were human or something. He caught hell for it. When the night's rituals ended, we were led to the cellar, still on hands and knees, where we were to sleep. The dog who stood up was swinging from a ceiling pipe, with his hands cuffed over the pipe and his jockstrap in his mouth with a piece of tape over it. His ankles were taped together, and he was not a happy puppy.

There were mattresses along the walls with ratty blankets spread on top. Our dog beds. A metal ring was set in the floor at the head of each bed. I'd noticed the rings in that room before, but I didn't know what they were for. With our hands and feet tied together, the dog collar around each neck was clipped to a chain, and connected to the ring in the floor with a D-ring. The bad dog was taken down and put to bed, with the jock still taped in his mouth.

Friday. My Life As A Dog. Up at dawn, or earlier. We were roused by the Suits and untied. Metal wrist and ankle shackles went on. They held our hands in front of us so that we could clean up the mess from the night before and cook breakfast for the Suits. There's an old joke about never frying bacon when you are naked. Well, frying it in a jockstrap isn't much better. We had to clean the breakfast dishes before we were freed to shower, dress and scarf down some cold table scraps.

The Suits told us not to remove the collars or the jockstraps. I wore the collar all day, as a badge of my pledge to the House, in spite of a few stares. We did break a rule. Prince and I exchanged collars to see if the Suits would notice. They didn't. Score one for the underdogs.

After dinner at the house, eaten from dog dishes, we were stripped shirtless. Some, me included, were tied to metal folding chairs and grilled on the points of frat history and legend. Others were taken out and exercised. In my exercise period, my pants were taken down and I had to piss against a tree, on all fours, by lifting a leg. Astro, a short muscular fellow with lots of hair, was allowed to run on his hind legs in order to catch and return the frisbees thrown by his masters. He had to catch them and bring them back in his mouth because his hands were tied behind his back. We all did our best to be doglike. I brought my friend Dave, one of the Suits, his newspaper and a pair of his old shoes in my mouth. "Good dog, Rinty," he said, and settled back with the Sun Times and a beer while I rested my head on the short hairs of his thigh and whimpered quietly. A risk, but my own dog does that to me all the time. Dave didn't flinch, he just stroked my hair a few times and said, "Good boy."

The drunker the Suits got, the rowdier and more abusive they got. They got us out of our pants and started spanking our asses with newspapers and paddles. We were taken to the cellar, tied up and gagged, and chained to the rings. Around 2 am, the Suits kicked us awake and carried us into the communal shower. God, they were drunk, and some of them weren't dressed. We ended up on the tile floor in the shower, still bound and gagged, and the Suits tried to drown us in a flood of beery piss. They shook their cocks dry and dared us to suck them off. Then the showers were turned on full blast, and we were soaked in cold, cold water. The bastards. At least the piss was washed away. They made a circus out of drying us with towels and portable dryers, but it was more a game of grab ass and squeeze balls. They felt us up, and I felt a finger up my ass, and they made jokes about our bodies and our penises, shrunken and wrinkled from the cold assault. It was back to the cellar, chained to the rings again, to sleep in bondage again.

Saturday. Let the Games Begin. We were split into two teams, Black and White, and we were given shorts in our team color. This would be the longest time we'd be untied while at the house that weekend. They called it the Greek Olympics, even though we were naked, and we had to compete in a number of sports in our shorts and dog collars, while our masters watched and cheered and got drunk. The field was muddy because the Suits had us turn the hoses on it that morning. The Suits would run out to trip us up, pull down our shorts, or bombard us with balls and water balloons.

I was on the Black Team, and we won when the scores were totalled. The Suits hosed us down, and gave us a ten minute break, total, to clean off the mud the hoses had missed. There was a mad rush of naked flesh in the shower, laughing and scrambling with each other for space and towels. We were told to report to the lounge for reward and punishment.

The dogs, Team Black and Team White, stood in the lounge, eyes looking at the floor, and hands behind our backs as they were tied. Team Black was gagged, and Team White blindfolded. Then we were blindfolded, too. The Suits told Team White to kneel, and a choir of drunken cheers went up in anticipation. Rough hands dragged us into position in front of our kneeling competitors, but we didn't know it at that moment. A hand took hold of the elastic bands on my shorts and jockstrap and pulled them down around my knees. The hand grabbed my cock and tugged on it. I joined my fellows in a chorus of "Mmmthfkkrr," which is gagged lingo for motherfucker. As the Suits hurled insults and applause, my cock found its way into somebody's mouth! One suit held me and pumped my groin into the mysterious mouth, while the other Suit held the Team white cocksucker in place. "Don't cum in their mouths or your ass is ours," an unseen Suit yelled. I was glad to hear a semblance of safe sex, even if our asses were theirs already. Didn't cum, but I was pretty damn stiff when my slickened cock was pulled from the mysterious mouth. The positions were reversed, our gags and clothes were removed, and I dropped to my knees and sucked a Team White member blindfolded. The Suits cheered us on. The cock came out of my mouth and I felt something warm and wet on my shoulder, but I didn't know if it was semen or spit. A few dogs had cum, in spite of the tension, though not in mouths, and the Suits gave them grief. "Fuckin' queers!" That kind of nonsense.

None of us, to my knowledge, found out who we sucked or who had sucked us.

The blindfolds came off and the opposing teams stood nose to nose and endured Suit hands whacking our behinds. I faced Prince. Had he sucked my cock? Had I blown him? Who knew? Prince smiled at me as we all were gagged again, black cloth for Team Black, white cloth for Team White. A Suit tied a thin rope around Prince's cock, and tied the other end around mine. The same for the other pairs of dogs as they faced each other.

There were maybe 10, 12 inches of rope separating Prince and me, so we had to walk sideways and in unison to avoid imminent castration. Not that the Suits made that process easy. Ouch! The dogs slept two per bed that night. Our feet were tied and then tied together. The collars were locked to the rings together and we lay there, face to gagged face, inches apart. The Suits laughed at the lovebirds, and sprayed beer on us. They lifted our bound hands and kicked at our helpless butts a few times. I headed to dreamland shortly thereafter, with Prince's forehead against mine.

Sunday. Open Sesame. Untied, we dogs were one team again as we went through our morning chores, stone naked and shackled, and still buzzing about what happened the previous night. There was more ritual grilling from the Suits on Greek rules and regs, and we were usually tied in whatever position the Suit in charge wanted. For awhile I was tied to a dining room chair. Later, a couple of Suits dragged me upstairs and tied me to a bed, face up, with outstretched arms and legs tied to the bedposts. I could swear the Suits were being less careful about concealing their own hard ons. A certain few were always pulling on the flies, as if to realign their underwear to accommodate something growing underneath.

Most of the Suits were looking more like Skins. Many were showing off bare chests and others were in shorts and barefoot as they continued to doghandle us. Like I said before, casual but firm, and so were the dogs.

Everyone gathered in the lounge for the finale. The Suits had tuxedo jackets and formal wear above the waist, and shorts and socks only below it. The Suits gagged us as we groaned "Not again." We were made to bend forward to touch our toes. In that position, our wrists were tied to our ankles.

Instead of the hooting and hollering we'd grown accustomed to, the Suits were eerily silent, watching. Between my legs, I saw a hairy pair of legs come up behind me. Our asses were greased with something, and then something hard started fucking our asses. It wasn't a hard Suit cock, though. All the dogs were being fucked with dildos in the shape of cocks. And big dildos, at that. The toys were rammed in as far up our shit chutes as possible.

With the symbolic fuck, the Suits grabbed their paddles and got wild and crazy again. Each Suit got three whacks on each ass cheek, as everyone counted our loud. A few used their swings to nail the dildo harder up my upturned ass.

We'd reached the end of our weekend ordeal. The Suits, now our brothers and more, untied and congratulated us, naked bodies, red asses and all, and we got stinking drunk.

MIDNIGHT RUN

For us, Hell Week at the House meant being treated like the lowest shits on earth. We were unquestionably at the Actives' command for personal and House chores. One Active got off on having me wipe his dick with toilet paper whenever he took a piss. I complained that that was queer shit. The Actives stripped me bareass naked and tied me to a sink stand until, as they said, I had "an attitude adjustment." They took my socks and stuffed them in my mouth. I got kicked, pissed on, splashed on, until I was willing and happy to lick the dick of the Active I had disobeyed and wipe it with toilet paper.

Pledges had to do forced exercise drills whenever the Actives felt like giving us a hard time. The drill was that we had to strip down to underwear or sometimes down to nothing, hit the floor and do fifty to one hundred pushups or situps, whatever was ordered. If you didn't or couldn't give them all the reps they wanted, the Actives tied and gagged you and gave you punishment licks across your ass till it was beet red.

When Hell Week was in session, the Actives found at least one reason to tie us up every day, and leave us tied and naked and embarrassed as hell. Bondage was the house special, and not only for asswipe pledges. Even Actives who seriously violated House rules were stripped to skivvies and tied to a chair or a door frame. I ought to know. As an Active and a hellraiser I spent a bunch of happy days half naked and gagged with a rag with my wrists chained to a hook on the ceiling.

The wildest Hell Week event at [Frat name] was the Midnight Run. Right after dinner, we were tied and gagged in our street clothes and locked in the lounge. Around midnight the Actives untied us, but just long enough for us to strip down to white cotton briefs in a hell of a hurry. They said the last pledge to strip would get gang fucked. Our hands were tied behind our backs and we were gagged with socks and black bandannas and loaded into a van for a short drive to the other side of campus. A few Actives rode with us to keep us in line, the rest followed in cars.

The destination was a wooded area and meadow on the fringe of campus. We were kicked out of the van as the Actives pinched our buttcheeks and snapped the elastic on our briefs. It's a funny feeling being nearly naked in front of a bunch of drunks with their clothes on. The rules were that we had to run across the meadow for the wooded area on the other side. The Actives would give us a ten second head start, then they'd come after us. If we made it to the woods without being caught, we'd be untied. If they caught us, "your asses are ours," they said. And they didn't untie us! We had to run barefoot across the field, in the dark, with hands tied and mouths gagged. We were really struggling with the ropes now, not sure about what was meant by the "your asses are ours" crack.

One Active blew a whistle and we ran for our lives like a flock of goony birds, perfectly humiliated and terrified. Using your arms helps you run faster, but our arms were no help to us bound. The mob of them swooped down on us in no time, teasing us a little and then tackling us to the ground, beating our butts and squeezing our defenseless dicks.

One pledge who was the best athlete of all actually made it to the other side. Instead of freedom, he was tied facing a tree, stripped nude and his butt was finger fucked and paddled while we were forced to watch. I thought his cock and stomach would be rubbed raw by the tree bark. The Active was a sadistic upper crust jerk, and you could see how much he enjoyed causing pain. He took the beer he'd been drinking and shoved the half empty bottle into the pledge's butt, saying that "[Frat name] doesn't need any smartasses."

The rest of us were huddled together on the ground, still bound, and we were pissed on and spat upon in the moonlight. We had to jog across the campus back to the House, bound and gagged and covered with slime, in full view of everyone who was still up and around at that hour. There were a lot of blushing teenagers making that run, especially when guys at other fraternities were giving us standing ovations. At least the run dried some of the piss and saliva. Pledges were bent across a table and held down while the Actives gave our butts what for with the pledge paddles. Those who had wriggled out of their ropes spent the night naked and hog-tied in the upstairs lounge, where they got the daylights molested out of them all night. The rest of us spent the night in naked bondage, but in slightly more comfortable spots, tied to beds and chairs. I was given two minutes to shower and towel off, then I reported butt naked to the Active whose dick I had refused to wipe clean. He tied my hands and had me on my knees between his thighs with lightning speed. Then he tied my ankles together and let me sleep with him in his bed.

SWIMMER INITIATED INTO FOOTBALL FRAT

🏛

The summer before my freshman year, I tore up my ankle after falling off a ladder. For rehabilitation, I was allowed to swim and ride the stationary bike, but I wasn't allowed to run on it until October. Riding a bike and going nowhere was always boring to me, so I decided to join the swim team in order to try to stay in shape for basketball. I had swum until I was sixteen, so I wasn't that bad, but my ankle prevented me from getting much spring when I dove or made a turn. Even though most of the team shaved their bodies before a meet, I didn't because I was only in events that I could easily score in team points. After practice, I would go to the training room for whirlpool and ice treatment on my ankle.

My roommate was a football player and I palled around with him a lot. This led to both of us getting invitations to join a frat that had a lot of football players as members and was considered the rowdiest on campus. Actually, it seemed to me that everyone was allowed to do their own thing, unlike some others that stressed conformity, including the frat that had the majority of basketball players. So I accepted.

Thursday afternoon after practice, I was whirlpooling my ankle when several of the swimmers walked in, grabbed me and said it was time for my initiation. I was carried, squirming, to the training table where I was taped spreadeagle face up to each of the legs with adhesive tape. A ball of tape was shoved in my mouth to keep me quiet and taped in with several more strips. One member of the team brought out a can of shaving cream and several razors and started applying the cream to my legs. I started squirming and actually broke the tape holding my right hand and started to try and get loose. My arm was grabbed and retaped to the leg in a position that if I moved, the arm would hurt. I was told that any more protests and they would also shave my head. They also applied shaving cream to my chest and arms. I still had my speedos on.

When they were finished with each limb, one at a time was untied, so all the hair could be removed. After they were done, the only hair I had was on top of my head and what was covered by the speedos. I was untied while each of them welcomed me as an official member of the swim team. It was getting late for dinner, so I quickly took off my trunks, put on a pair of sweats and sneaks and hustled as best I could to dinner.

When I got back to the dorm a note was on the door from my roommate Wayne saying there was a frat meeting for all pledges at 7:30. I was the only non-football player they accepted during my pledge class, so everyone else had been told at practice. Being with the swim team, I did not see the football team as we practiced in a separate building from the main gym.

Since I got delayed earlier, I did not find the note until almost 7:30 pm and it was a 10 minute walk to the frat house. I had to walk, too, because my ankle was still too sore to jog. I got there around 7:45, and after going thru the "why are you late" routine a couple of times, I was allowed into the clubhouse where the pledge class was lined up, standing at attention, stripped to their undershorts. I was immediately told to do the same. I had a sickening feeling as I hadn't had time to change from my sweats, but not wanting to get in any more trouble I stripped the sweatpants off and stood there bare-ass naked.

There were still red marks on my ankles and wrists from being tied up earlier along with some dried blood from being shaved and none of this escaped the attention of my new brothers. They did make the other pledges strip their shorts off so we would all look the same.

The reason we were lined up was so the auction of the pledge class could be held. Each pledge was bought by a brother. The money raised would go to financing a party or some other worthy project of the fraternity. The problem was the more that was spent on purchasing the pledge, the worse he was going to have it since the brother would want to get his money's worth. It was also not uncommon for the pledges to be resold during the pledge period to recoup some of the investment along with having some fun. Although the pledge period didn't start until the following week, it was decided at football practice to start early since the brothers wanted to let off some steam before the game on Saturday.

I figured that since I was an "outsider," my ass would be fairly safe. Not that many members knew me very well because my classes and swimming did not provide much contact with the football players. I calculated wrong. Part of the auction was the "softening of the beef" to show how much you could take, plus provide an energy release for the brothers. When it was my turn, I was told to "assume the position." Beefo, a defensive lineman, took the paddle and smacked me a good one. I "landed" about ten feet away. Beefo was a muscular hulk about 240 lbs and I weighed only 175 and was fairly thin so it was a total mismatch. The brothers accused me of trying to get away, so noticing the marks on my wrists and ankles, they figured I liked to be tied up so some rope was found, my hands were tied in front of me, the rope was thrown over a rafter and I was pulled up to my toes. I was then paddled six or more times. I don't really know. I was too hurting to count.

They wanted to see how far my legs would fly when hit. I had pleaded for them to stop after three or four hits, so they gagged me with another pledge's shorts and taped it in with a roll of adhesive tape. By the time the paddling ended, I was crying; my ass hurt like hell and my wrists hurt from swinging on them.

As I was auctioned, someone mentioned that my body was as smooth as a baby's. After that comment was made, a bidding war developed between Rick, the starting safety and kick returner, and the running back, Ed. Both were hard-nosed players and I knew then that I was going to be in for a rough time. Rick bought me and instead of letting me down, got two more pieces of rope, tied them around my ankles and had two pledges pull on the ropes to spread my legs. Rick then instructed my roommate to get some shaving cream and razor from his room. He stated that he didn't know of any babies that had hair on their ass or crotch, so his baby wasn't going to have any either. I tried to yell, but got the paddle again until I stopped.

When Wayne got back (he wasn't allowed to dress to get the stuff and he had to go outside to get to Rick's room!) Rick forced Wayne to finish shaving my body. Any hair that was found on my body after the shave would result in punishment for Wayne. So he took great care in lathering me up and shaving me. The combination of the warm lather on my sore ass and cock, and Wayne moving my cock around to get all the hair made me hard. This caused me to get the paddle again as babies can't get hard.

I was left tied to the rafters for the rest of the auction, although my feet were untied so I could stand easily. When the meeting ended, Rick took me down, but kept my wrists tied and the gag in place, took me outside and over to his room where I was given his rules for the pledge period. Then I was allowed to put my sweats on and go back to my room. This ended a very interesting day and I knew my ass was going to look like hell, along with my wrists, for the swim meet on Saturday. And the pledge period hadn't even officially started yet.

THE POST
AND THE RACK

🏛

I pledged to a jock frat at a university in Dixie, and old tradition called for the verbal and physical humiliation of humble pledges. A few years before I arrived, they'd gotten into trouble after leaving the pledges naked and tied to headstones in a graveyard one rainy night, and one guy got pneumonia from the experience and nearly croaked. The town and the cemetery weren't amused, either. So the frat limited its rope 'em and gag 'em activity to one night only, on its own property.

For the big night, we were given a strict, no substitute dress code. We had to wear white dress shirts, the red bow ties we'd worn at the Greek Carnival, denim shorts, and nothing else. No coats, shoes, socks or even underwear.

As the pledges arrived, "promptly, or else," we were each given a number and ordered out of our shirts, but were told to keep the bowties on. Commanded to kneel, our hands and feet were tied up with rope. I was the sixth to arrive, so my number was six, and one guy held me down as the number "6" was scrawled on my chest in lipstick. Since there was nothing I could do about it, they coated my lips with the stuff, too, and all the other pledges got painted with lipstick just like me.

Our would-be masters had dressed for their parts. The officers wore long magicians' robes with little or nothing underneath. The pledge chairman and some others were mostly stripped to the waist. Some dressed like the guards of a harem in an Arabian Nights movie, complete with turbans and fake scimitars, while others just wore microshorts that gave new meaning to the word codpiece.

One guy lifted me by the shoulders, another grabbed my feet, and I was carried into the library room along with all the other pledgeboys. They left us groaning and chuckling on the floor and told us to keep quiet and wait our turn.

I rolled around on the floor with my fellow numbers. In spite of all the macho posturing, we were a bunch of scared boys barely out of high school, tied up and practically naked, and imagining the worst. I'd heard stories that a black fraternity on campus tied their pledges to a post nude and branded them.

The door swung open. "Number One, prepare for the Test," a voice rang out. The voice belonged to Ed, the sergeant at arms, nicknamed Ed the Bed because of his alleged prowess with women. Ed the Bed and a guy we nicknamed Dolph picked up Number One and untied his feet. Dolph was wearing a black neckerchief, which he removed and gagged Number One with as we watched. Number One was led away, gagged and struggling.

Numbers Two through Five were gagged and taken away when their turns came, about every five or ten minutes, and they didn't return, either. Pledge Number Seven nudged me with his toes and said "You're next. Don't bend over or they'll rape the shit out of you." He was kidding, and I laughed.

"Number Six, prepare for the Test," Ed called out. He pulled me to my feet with a "Get up, boy!" and Dolph gagged me with a black neckerchief before I could lodge a complaint. Mmmmfff! When my feet were freed, I was hustled out to face the unknown, accompanied by a few shouts of encouragement from my remaining brother numbers.

Ed and Dolph said nothing as they held on to my arms and took me upstairs. Dolph was nude from the waist up, and wore an executioner's hood. Ed was also hooded, and he had on a black tanktop and black shorts with a pair of handcuffs connected to his beltloops, holding the shorts up. If they were trying to intimidate me, they were doing a good job.

We entered the Examination Room, actually the third floor lounge. The darkened room was lit by candles, and some eerie classical music was playing. I could see four other guys in their codpiece shorts holding candles and standing silent guard, along with two frat officers in long robes and turbans. The furniture had been removed, but something new had been added. A heavy wooden post stood waiting for me in the center of the room. Just off to the side, Pledge Number Five lay belly down on a long table that, in the darkness, looked like a medieval rack. His outstretched hands and feet were roped to the four corners. He had been stripped nude, except for the bowtie, gagged, and he looked at me with a scared shitless expression.

"Bind the supplicant to the post," said Brio, one of the barefoot officers in a long robe. Ed and Dolph untied my hands and then bound them behind the wooden post. Ed unfastened my shorts and yanked them from my legs. Now I was as nude as Number Five, a few feet away. I sputtered uselessly into the gag as Brio flicked at my dick with his thumb and forefinger.

For the Test, I had to answer a series of questions to their satisfaction. I was told what would happen if my answers weren't good enough. "Number Five failed to answer a question," Brio said, mock-ominously. "Observe, Number Six, the punishment for failure." Ed and Dolph picked up their paddles and I watched with alarm as a terrified Number Five got his butt double-spanked hard! He took the first few blows, but by the end he was twisting and making guttural sounds through his gag. Number Five was released, his hands were bound behind him and he was led away, still moaning.

Ed took off my gag, and the officers fired questions at me, things like the Greek alphabet backwards, stuff about the history of the university and the frat, the true status of pledges, and weird stuff like naming the capitals of South Dakota and Liechtenstein. Pierre and Vaduz, for any future frat victims reading this. I'd studied, and with as much macho bravado as I could muster while nude and tied to a post, I spat back the answers. The right answers, followed by the polite but firm salutation, "Sir!"

I felt good, and I knew I'd be untied and greeted outside the door with maybe a beer and hopefully my clothes. Nope. The black gag went back in my mouth, and I was taken down from the post and tied face down on the rack, like Number Five had been. You see, you got tied to the rack whether or not you answered the questions correctly. And as I had watched Number Five get paddled, he'd watched Number four get his, and so on. And Number Five had known what was in store, just like I now knew what was coming.

Ed and Dolph had gone to fetch Number Seven, while Brio rubbed and patted my upturned ass. "Fresh meat, gentlemen," he said, as the vergers holding the candles laughed in approval. Oh, brother. The rack was damp with the sweat and lipstick smudges left by Numbers One thru Five, and I knew Number Seven would be lying in my sweat next.

When Number Seven came in, bound and gagged, he saw me and he briefly fought to escape, but they had him nude and bound to the post in no time. Brio went through the same routine, explaining what would happen to Number Seven if he fucked up the Test and using me as an example. I got my ten or twelve from

Ed and Dolph's paddles, tried to take it quietly but was moaning and groaning by the last blow, an openhand slap on my red asscheek from Ed's hand. Released from the makeshift rack, Ed bound my hands behind my back again and led me out, still gagged and glancing back at Number Seven. Ed took hold of my balls and dick and pulled me behind him, warning that he'd twist them off if I didn't keep up.

He dragged me downstairs, through the kitchen and out to the back yard, where my fellow pledge numbers and the rest of the frat were gathered. The other five pledges lay next to each other on the ground, faces up, still bound and gagged. Their bodies had been arranged in a row, side by side, with Number One's head laying next to Number Two's feet, Number Two's gagged head between the feet of One and Three, and so on. Imagine the way you'd put batteries in a radio, positive, negative, positive, negative, but with the batteries lined up side by side and pointing in opposite directions, and you'll get the picture.

The pledges were bunched together so that the sides of their bodies were touching. I was placed next to Number Five, toes pointing in the opposite direction and my head next to his feet. My own feet were roped together, as the others' ankles had been, and we were ordered to lie still by our laughing, drunken masters. Soon, Number Seven was next to me, with his size thirteen gunboat feet in my face, then Number Eight went next to him, and so on, till there were ten scared, naked guys in bowties all tied up with no place to go, and getting the horselaugh from the frat. The assembled multitude, some dressed, most practically undressed, formed a circle around us. The pledge chairman said we were so worthless that only the power of the Delta moon, whatever that was, could save the honor of the fraternity.

The frat linked arms and began their chants to invoke the infinite to make us fit for membership. It was wild, all these half-undressed guys chanting and shaking, boozing it up while a couple pulled down their shorts and shot their version of the Delta "moon" our way, yelling "Kiss it, you fucks!" It was like an old South revival meeting. When the yells reached a peak, we pledges were doused in a sea of beer from buckets, pitchers, plastic cups and cans that the frat had hidden behind them while we were tied up on the ground. At least I hope it was beer, at least that's how it smelled and tasted as it filtered through the gag. We were left to struggle in the muddy mess for awhile, until we were hosed down and finally carried back inside and untied.

GAGGED PLEDGES STAND GUARD

As a pledge at Sigma Etc. Etc. at dear old Anonymous University, I did my share of bondage servitude. Our rear ends were paddled raw, and we were bound and gagged in a score of painfully creative positions. We wore leg irons and wrist shackles on our usually practically bare bodies to perform the household chores. Our uniform was kind of a loincloth, dyed blue, that covered crotch and ass but left the sides of your ass exposed for public abuse. When we weren't serving the actives with chores, we served them by being tied and gagged to anything nailed down, and sometimes we were just bound to each other. Cocksucking was an ancient tradition at Sigma House, and those who hadn't learned how to do it in high school earned a doctorate in the subject by the end of freshman year.

At Sigma, bound pledges were once forced to suck each other's cock until we came, while the actives watched. We also got tied to chairs and were forced to piss on ourselves after not going to the bathroom all day and after being force fed a number of beers. My Big Brother's favorite pastime was tying me up and taking a leak on me in the john. We were spat on, burned with cigarettes, we were bound hands-over-head to posts and had all body hair shaved except for the Mohawk haircut they gave us. It was a humiliating, debasing, painful, abusive, sloppy, horny, erotic, cock hardening roped and gagged experience. I'd do it again in two seconds.

Of course, once we baby Sigs came into manhood as full fledged brothers, we could spend the next three years making life miserable, or wonderful, for future freshman pledges. Tie 'em up, gag their silly mouths and have fun, and we did.

Our house has a longstanding rivalry with the neighbors across the quad, the hapless boys of Pi — —, hereafter known as Pike. In junior year, we decided to add a new wrinkle to Hell Week. We obtained the names and particulars of the Pike pledges and invited them to a friendly, "get to know ya" party at Sigma House, and made it sound as if all pledges campus wide were expected to attend. We did have a house party, and eight gullible Pike pledges showed up and became the party favors. As they arrived and identified themselves, each one was captured and hustled into the basement, with a hand over his mouth. We relieved them of their clothing, down to their briefs, and bound and gagged them on the carpet. They tried to struggle and scream, but they were ours for the night. Two of them brought friends to the party, both pledges to other frats, and they got tied up just as tight. One of the friends wasn't wearing underwear so it was just too bad for him that he got tied up naked.

We had a total of ten guys moaning and writhing on the floor. The pesky ones who gave us the most trouble got their hands and feet tied together and their balls mashed. We didn't neglect our own pledges, either. They served as silent guards in their loincloths. They proudly wore the wrist and ankle shackles, and they'd been gagged with a big brother's underwear or socks, so they couldn't help being silent! Their assignment was to keep the Pike pledges in line, by any means possible. One Sig pledge kept his bare foot on the gagged mouth of a particularly loud Pike groaner, to keep him quiet. Another of ours knelt down, shackles and all, and sat on a guy's ass to keep him still.

Another hour into the drunken party, and the Pike pledges

were sweaty and resigned to the evening's fate. That didn't stop us from spanking and paddling some pledge boy ass. We took pictures of our guests with an instant camera, and made up a mock ransom note with letters cut from magazines. We promised Pike that we'd show their pledges the tortures of the damned unless they agreed to our boneheaded list of self-serving demands. The note and pictures were delivered, and when Pike called to investigate, we dragged a pledge to the phone and let him grunt a few times. Pike guys were somewhere in the middle of the evolutionary ladder, they've probably slipped a rung since then, but even they knew a gagged grunt. Besides, Pike had a bondage initiation rep, too.

Victory seemed our very own, but this tale has a twist. Our house vice president left the house to visit his girlfriend, and on the way he was seized by some Pike boys. Foolish man. We got a call that they had tied him up, and sure enough we received a polaroid snap of our v.p., a brown-haired beauty with a two digit IQ, naked and lying on his side with his ankles hogtied to his wrists and a wide strip of leather filling and surrounding his mouth.

We had to do something. Pledges were expendable, of course, but we had to rescue our brother even if he was an idiot. We worked out a hostage exchange. Both frats would bring their prisoners to the quad at midnight. Very melodramatic. Very *Spy Who Came in from the Cold.*

As a parting gesture, we untied the Pike pledges' feet and relieved them of their underwear. They'd just have to make that long walk across the quad buck naked. Ropes were tied around their necks and our pledges, their wrists unshackled but not their legs, led them into that good night, not so gently. What a riot! The half naked leading the naked, all tied up and getting whistles and jeers from curious onlookers in other houses. It was a drunken event out of Animal

House. Three Pike pledges we hadn't captured carried out our v.p., still tightly bound and gagged and nude. We made the trade and carried the party into the quad for awhile, while a lot of nervous, naked pledges milled around, struggling and begging to be untied. They succeeded only in getting themselves jostled and getting their half erect cocks squeezed.

Eventually, we went back to our houses before campus security could rouse from its torpor and investigate the noise. We tied up our pledges, Pike tied up its pledges, and peace reigned in the valley. The Sigs took a vote and we decided to keep the v.p. tied and gagged all night for being stupid enough to get caught. For his bed, we had him stretch out on the couch, and I mean really stretch, with his hands pulled way over his head and tied to one end, his feet tied to the other, and all muscles in between stretched and taut. Meanwhile, I tied my little brother face down to the bed, and my roommate and I got naked and paddled him. It's what scumbag pledges need and deserve. Then I tied him on on the floor and he slept there, knowing he would suck our cocks on the morrow. If I'd tried to fuck him, my roommate, in spite of the fact that he liked having our pet pledge suck him, would have gone into heterosexual apoplexy. Double standards make no sense. But he loved getting sucked in the morning, and so did I. And our pet pledge loved to do it. He had no choice.

Just another day at Sigma House.

SHARING
A DOG DISH

Thanks to fraternity bondage, I got to know and love my best buddy Gary as we shared a dog dish of chili. We were two of a bunch of half naked pledges, naked except for our tight cotton briefs. We were kneeling on the floor with our hands cuffed behind us and our feet in shackles, wearing choke chains and slurping up some greasy chili from dog dishes, two to a dish. Naturally, as you bent down to eat, your butt rose and an Active would whack it with a belt or a shoe. Sometimes they'd pull down our briefs and smack our bare, rosy butts. Usually, your face would smash into the food or collide with the hapless pledge sharing your dish. That's what happened with me and Gary. We butted heads after someone smacked my naked butt.

I didn't know Gary well because we'd only exchanged a few brief words till then. But right after we collided, he gave me such a sweet, goofy chili-covered smile that I developed an instant crush on this cute eighteen-year-old kid cuffed and shackled in his briefs next to me, and it turned into a long term friendship. It developed as we were tied and gagged to posts, bound to chairs and spreadeagle/ gagged on the rec room floor, always in white cotton briefs. The only time we were stripped naked was when we received our traditional paddling. Nude, next to Gary, our hands were tied over our heads as we faced a wall, and we were gagged with tape across our mouths. Our Masters paddled our butts raw, over and over. Even Gary had a hard on after that whipping.

PAINT OFF
AND PISS OFF

🏛

Bright college days. I attended a university on the West Coast, and was encouraged by a friend to pledge at a fraternity.

Our pledgemasters believed in bondage as the ultimate humiliation. Nothing overtly sexual happened—no one was tied to a tree, rip-stripped and gang-raped by the football team and the thumbwrestling squad—but you don't spend all that time in the frat, nearly naked and all tied up, without thinking that someone doing the tying is enjoying this beyond the limits of simple ritual.

Hell Week seemed more like Hell Decade, but I loved it. Even before the week officially started, both me and my roomie, fellow-pledge and good hometown friend named John, found ourselves manhandled, tied and humiliated. Soon after we moved into the house, our pledgemasters gave their charges the task of painting the TV lounge. We were all given a pair of grey running shorts with the frat's greek lettering on the side, and were told that the shorts were the only clothing we could wear while painting the room. If the paint splattered our bare skin, too damn bad.

The paint job began the next day at an assigned time after classes. Unfortunately for John, his last class ran too long, and he was late getting back to the house. He tried sneaking in—he wore the shorts under his clothes and dumped the outer garments in the hall—but he was caught and punished. We watched as pledgemasters Ken and Nick backed John against a stepladder, and planted his bare feet on the first rung. A couple of pledges were ordered to tie John's feet to the sides of the ladder with duct tape. His arms were lifted over his head, and each wrist was tied to the top of the ladder. Another piece of tape sealed his mouth, and more tape was wrapped around his waist and groin to prevent him from falling.

As the rest of us painted, John moaned and struggled and nearly knocked the ladder over a couple of times. Occasionally we had to climb up the other side of the ladder to reach the high spots on the wall. It was a kick to climb the ladder and see John's bound legs and back helplessly pressed against the opposite rungs.

We were "encouraged" by our Masters to spill paint on John. In short order, his bound body and hair were streaked with blue paint. He began to look like a Druid, bound and gagged and ready for dawn sacrifice at Stonehenge to appease the eclipse god. John strained and twisted his bod to avoid each new assault, but the tape held him fast.

When we finished painting, I was ordered to cut John from the ladder. The tape yanked some of the hair from his wrists and legs. He nearly collapsed in my arms for a moment or so, but I held onto his waist and helped him upstairs, getting some of the not-quite dry paint on my skin. The evening's entertainment was capped as our frat brothers laughed at John and me sitting in the shower trying to scrub off the paint with the strongest soap we could find. We got most of our bodies clean, although John had blue spots on his toes and among the hairs above his right nipple for days.

During initiation, John and I and the other pledges were

roused from a sound sleep as our brothers-to-be burst into our rooms. They ripped off John's pajamas and my underwear, and held us down while blindfolding us and tying our hands in front. Using the end of the rope as a leash, they pulled me to my feet and led/dragged me and my nude brethren down the stairs to the basement, where my hands were raised and tied to some sort of hook attached to an overhead beam in the center of the chilly rec room. The blindfold cut off my sight, but occasionally I rubbed against other naked, trembling bodies on both sides of me, so I figured the pledge class had been tied standing side by side, with our wrists bound over our heads.

It wasn't a high ceiling and I'm relatively tall, so by stretching a bit I could keep my feet more or less squarely on the floor, but I learned later that a couple of my shorter brothers were literally dangling from the hooks, trying to stand on their toes to relieve the pressure on their wrists. We were ordered to keep quiet by our Pledge Masters, as they and the rest of the frat (and for all I knew, the entire population of the Pacific Northwest) laughed and hooted and pinched and slapped and taunted us about the states of our shivering bodies tied and hung like sides of beef, and about the erect cocks that were beginning to rear their heads, including mine.

The ceremony of words began with the usual quasi-mystical, pseudo-Druidical nonsense about making worthless sacks of shit such as we worthy to join the men of their estimable brotherhood—chants I can't reveal at length without torture and despair beyond imagination. After asking us a few taunting questions, they got out their paddles, and you could almost hear us tightening our asses, bracing for the pain. Each pledge was to receive "ten good ones"—more if we fucked up—and we were promised an additional lick or four if the spirit moved our Masters. It would.

The anticipation was heightened by not knowing where or when the spanking would begin. Then I heard the air whistling through the holes in the paddle, followed by a sharp slap on the ass of a pledge somewhere off to my right. The rest of us writhed in our helpless bondage, much to the delight of our drunken audience.

We were to count each stroke, eg. one Master, two Master, etc. But midway through his paddling, the first pledge started screaming and crying and begged to be untied. Big mistake. Nobody disrupts the ceremony in mid-spank. "Shut that fucker up," I heard someone say. "He'll wake up the whole campus!" The voice of Pledge Master Nick said, "I think I'll gag the son of a bitch."

I heard someone tear off a piece of duct tape and slap it across the pledge's mouth, stifling his cries into muffled moans. Then Pledge Master Nick helpfully suggested, "Hell, let's gag all these fuckin' crybabies!" The hoots and cheers among the brothers sealed our fates, and our mouths. Pledge Master Ken grabbed me by the shoulders and whispered, "This won't hurt. Much," as he sealed my mouth with the tape gag.

The spankings continued, as the pledge who'd broken down got the ten he'd been promised and then some. We were still ordered to count the licks audibly, and the frat members laughed as our countings were muffled by the gags. A hand touching my ass, followed by a sudden swing from the paddle, told me that it was my turn for ten. The pain made me weak! I involuntarily shifted from side to side to avoid the blows, but Ken's aim was true. I finally screamed, "Ten, Master!" through the gag, and got another lick just for the hell of it.

After the paddling, the gags were torn from our mouths, ripping out more than a few moustache hairs. While still tied to the ceiling hooks, we were forced to eat something vile (rumored to be dog shit but actually some sort of gelatinous oatmeal concoction), followed by a long, bladder-stretching swig of bourbon and beer. That late-night snack completed the ceremony for the evening, and the Pledge Masters untied our hands from the hooks.

Before I could remove the blindfold, someone forced my hands behind my back and tied them together. Another rope went around my feet, and the noises and moans I could hear told me that the other pledges were getting the same treatment.

Someone grabbed my shoulders and not so gently dragged me across the floor and deposited me on a large sheet of slick rubber coated with something that smelled like cooking oil. I squirmed on the slippery surface and felt another naked pledge next to me, and then another. They piled the bunch of us in a heap of bound, oily bodies. Pledge Master Nick's voice told us that this was our last night as "pansies," so we should spend one last night together. Before our torturers left, we were ordered not to try to remove our bonds, and to keep quiet. As we were blindfolded with our feet tied, we weren't going anywhere, anyway.

In total darkness, there was nothing to do but get comfortable in the slippery mess, as we bumped into and slid off of each other's slickened chests, legs, butts and cocks. The paddling and the liquor had subdued us, but I felt my heart beating with fear and excitement. I could hear a couple of my fellow prisoners talking or on the verge of tears.

I recognized the voice of my roommate and closest college friend, John, who was lying next to me. We talked for a bit about the night's activities. He had been truly frightened by the whole thing and was almost sobbing. And in an uncharacteristic move (John is as straight as the short line between points A and B), he pressed his bound body against mine and continued to cry softly.

As a footnote to this part of the story, when Pledge Master Ken and the others came to untie us the next morning, one of the bound pledges had managed to work off his blindfold during the night. For his initiative, pledge Dave's arms were hoisted over his head toward the ceiling hooks again, and he got five good paddles on his butt as the rest of us watched. Even after releasing all of us and allowing us to get cleaned and dressed, Dave spent much of that day in some form of bondage, forced to stand in the front doorway with his hands tied behind his back or tied to a chair during mealtimes.

Each Pledge Master was assigned two pledges for the initiation/hazing process. John and I (we became closer friends after that first night) were the responsibility of Pledge Master Ken. Each master could assign his charges any method of his own devising (within reason) to degrade and prepare us to join the brotherhood. Besides the usual "wash my car, lick my feet, get me another beer" business, Ken had a fixation on bondage as the ultimate humiliation. John and I spent a lot of that week tied up. One night, we had to serve dinner and bus tables while wearing makeshift ankle "shackles"—a piece of rope was tied to each foot with a short length in between, forcing us to take short steps (or else fall on our faces).

Later that night, while John was in his bed and I was doing

some late-night studying on mine, Ken and a couple of his henchmen pulled a surprise room inspection. He pronounced our room a pit (a matter of opinion that allowed no discussion) and said we would be punished. Over our loud protests, one henchman seized my arms and forced me onto my bed, while the other pulled John from his bed and pushed him face down onto mine. All I had on was a pair of sweatpants, while John was only wearing his briefs.

My hands and feet were tied with short lengths of rope, and I was gagged with a bandana. I stared at John, a few inches away from my head, who was being equally manhandled. We were left on the bed, side by side, bound and struggling. One of the henchmen stroked our hair and blew us a kiss, and then he stood by our open door for over an hour and invited passers-by to look in and see what a "shit pit" looked line. I've never been much of an exhibitionist, but I'll admit that I enjoyed getting glances from bemused, half-naked guys on their way to the showers.

One afternoon, Pledge Master Ken didn't approve of my attitude, so he tied my hands behind a floor-to-ceiling post in the Common Room, until he was convinced that I had re-learned the proper respect. With my back against the post and the rope cutting into my wrists (those ropes were *tight*), I was feeling hotter than even Ken would've dreamt in his philosophy.

A few days after the Paint-Off came the Piss-Off. One night, a guard was posted in front of the bathrooms. His job was to turn away any pledges who wanted to use the john after dinner. We knew they were up to something. We were also forbidden to leave the house, so we couldn't even relieve ourselves on a tree.

Around 10 pm, we were ordered to the basement rec room.

The older brothers were waiting for us, and the smell of booze and reefer in the air told us we were in for trouble. Our pledgemasters greeted us with the usual round of curses, then they told us to remove our shirts, shoes and socks, but leave our pants on. We complied, accompanied by the hoots and catcalls of our drunken/stoned brethren. Our hands were tied in front of us, a piece of duct tape was slapped over our mouths, and we were blindfolded with black cloth. They led us to the center of the large room, turned us slightly, and stretched our arms above our heads, tying our hands to the same hooks from which we'd been suspended when we received our first paddling of Hell Week. I could feel someone's shoulder blades and ass against mine, and toes would step on my feet. I figured out (and it was confirmed later) that we were tied close together in a single-file line of frat flesh in groups of two, with each of the two turned to face each other. I learned later that my "partner" that night was Ian, a green-eyed blond from Britain.

I hung there, nervous and excited. Then I heard giggling, followed by a scuffling sound behind me. A hand grabbed my left foot and tied it to Ian's right foot, and vice-versa. I still remember how scratchy those ropes felt against our ankles. Our legs were tied together in the same manner, below the knees. By pulling me closer to Ian, I was forced to stretch my torso ahead of my bound arms and lean back slightly, creating an uncomfortable pull on my shoulders. The muffled moans of discomfort told me that my brother pledges were in the same predicament. Another rope cinched our waists together, grinding our groins into each other.

That's when the main event began. A pair of hands slithered in between our crotches. Quickly, nimble fingers unzipped my jeans and reached in to grab my cock. I yelled into the gag and bucked and twisted, but I was blind and helpless. I could hear the cries of the other pledges, and I knew I wasn't alone in this torture. As the hand squeezed my cock, I could feel the other hand unzipping Ian's pants and fishing for his penis. Ian's writhing nearly pulled my arms from their sockets, as he fought to protect his balance and his family jewels.

My cock was not-so-gently inserted through Ian's fly (scraping painfully on his zipper in the process), and I felt a foreign penis positioned against my balls in my pants.

After calling for quiet, pledgemaster Ken made a rambling speech, about the sacred bonds of fraternity being so strong that a brother would gladly accept another brother's urine. Therefore, we were ordered to piss in each other's pants, and bathe our brethren in precious bodily fluids, or something like that. Now I understood the bathroom embargo. Laughter exploded, and you could almost make out the muffled "NOs" through the gags. Ian seemed to be trying to maneuver his cock out of my pants, but the ropes held our legs together, and he only succeeded in rubbing his cock against mine and getting them both even harder.

The sooner we pissed, we were told, the sooner we'd be released. It had been several hours since we'd heeded nature's call—not an eternity, but our bladders were full. But it was a bit like taking a piss at the doctor's office to give a urine sample—it took a while to get things flowing. To the chants of "GO-GO-GO!," one of the pledges began the piss parade. I'd never been pissed on before (or since, thank you), but I figured I could take it better than my partner, who seemed on the edge of total freakout. So I held back until he delivered his wet load.

The warm stream splashed against my balls and the bottom of my ass, then raced down my legs and soaked my jeans. We both squirmed nervously as Ian's piss soaked our bound feet in a small puddle. As he finished, I let go with my contribution, soaking his underwear and all points below his waist.

Eventually they untied us, but not before some of the guys used our bound bodies and feet for their own toilet target practice. Not only did the place smell like a public toilet, it was getting downright slippery.

They removed the blindfold first, and the first things I saw were Ian's eyes smiling at me in what looked like nervous laughter.

When we were freed, none of us had time to dwell on guilt and shame. Instead, our Masters handed us mops and buckets and told us to clean up the mess. Cleanliness is next to impossible.

A few days later, after being told that we were to help unload some party supplies from Ken's ancient VW bus, John and I were seized on our way to the vehicle, rolled on the ground, bound hand and foot and gagged, and stuffed into the rear of the van. We were both wearing shirts and shorts, but John had left the house without putting on his sandals (we didn't know we'd be going on a trip), and as Ken and his friends drove us to our unknown destination, I spent the trip nuzzled next to John's roped bare feet. I don't know what we would've done if the police had stopped Ken for speeding, but with my mouth gagged, I wouldn't have done much talking, anyway.

We arrived at a deserted corner of a county park, and John and I were dragged onto the grass. Without removing our other bonds, they retied us sitting back to back by tying our arms together, and looped the same rope around our chests a couple of times. We were helpless, immobile, and in public.

I thought they were going to leave us there to fend for ourselves in the middle of nowhere. Instead, Ken and the others took positions around us and began a lecture on the finer points of the history and traditions of the frat—points that we were to memorize and recite later that week. It was an absurd theatre in the round, but boy, did we listen. Being bound and gagged and at the mercy of quasi-sadists in the middle of nowhere is a great way to command your attention.

The following Saturday, after a few hours of forced yard work, Ken decided to "wash the stink" from us by ordering us into a shower stall. Facing each other, John and I got our hands tied together. They were lifted slightly above us and tied to the shower head with strips of cloth. Ken turned the knob marked "C" and our writhing bodies were drenched by freezing water. At least it was better than being boiled by scalding H_2O.

There are other bondage incidents at the frat house—such as the time I returned from classes to discover pledgemaster Ken and his minion hog-tying my roommate "for the hell of it." I was ordered to help them, and when we had him trussed like a prize steer, they turned around and hog-tied my wrists to my ankles, and used John's socks to gag me.

As well as physical bondage, the fraternity played mindgames to keep us in emotional bondage. Besides the expected humiliations, it was ordered that throughout Hell Week, pledges were not allowed to wear shirts at meal times or other specified occasions. It was one more way of emphasizing our less-than-zero status. It also gave our Masters a golden opportunity to write things such as "fuckhead," "shit for brains" and "queer bait" on our naked chests in lipstick.

Of course, by surrendering so much control and accepting this treatment almost gratefully, we were actually in the driver's seat. Any one of us could've stopped it, or run away, or gone to the administration or the school media and raised holy hell. But we didn't.

BULL MILKING CONTEST

I lived as a boy in a small town in the Middle West & was always a loner. When I went to college in a nearby town I was very flattered to be asked to join a frat. But I didn't know what to expect. How green can a guy be? We had not had PE in school so I had never been nude in front of other guys before, nor seen guys nude. Anyway, I was told to meet a truck on Friday evening for a "get-together." Bring nothing & wear only what could be seen. I still didn't suspect anything. So I met the truck. It was one of those that have ribs over it to hold up a tarp.

Two guys (members) were in the back, with more in the front to drive. I got up into the back of the truck and my hands were tied spreadeagle to one of the supports "So I wouldn't fall when the truck was moving." Of course my asking them to please not do this to me only got a "You want to belong, don't you?" and of course I did so I shut up. Three more guys joined us & each were tied as I was. The truck started moving in the direction of town and right away the two members dragged our pants around our ankles. So there we stood, tied hands spread out helpless and nekkid from the waist down. I don't think I was ever so embarrassed & of course I got a hard on which I was kidded about. One of the guys really put up a howl & they put a rag in his mouth with tape to keep him quiet & we were taken down Main Street. From there we were taken out in the country to a barn with a nice river running nearby.

I don't remember just what all & in what order things took place except I do remember being nekkid all weekend & tied up in some way.

On one night, Friday I think, they tied me spreadeagle on my back, with a blindfold on so I couldn't see a thing. Don't know how many there were that were around me but they started in on me with feathers, hands, sticks, not real sure but anyway they were tickling me I thought I would lose my mind & wasn't tied too tight so could wiggle around some, but they wouldn't leave me alone from the soles of my feet to the top of my head, ears, nose, under arms, knees, cock & balls. I guess my begging finally paid off as they stopped. Stopped the tickling, that is. Then they started pulling hairs out of my body. One at a time. I don't have much body hair so most of their play was at my crotch. Every time they pulled a hair it would itch and of course I couldn't scratch.

They tired of that game & left me alone for a while. Still tied & blindfolded. After a while how long I have no idea now they put another guy on top of me belly to belly. They had his hands tied behind him. They pulled his legs apart so they could get to his balls, of course my legs were already tied spread eagle. They now tied our balls together & let his legs go & started to tickle him. I thought I would lose my balls that night but they didn't tickle him very long but left us tied by our balls for the rest of the night. We didn't get a lot of sleep tied up that way.

The next day seemed like a long day. We had to do a lot of the things most frat initiations do like getting our asses paddled for missing a question, any little thing, calling our masters "Sir,"— things like that. But there were also other things to do. They had a table in the middle of the room where we were made to get up one at a time on our hands & knees. They tied our hands & knees to the corners of the table & told us this was the Bull Milking Contest.

We had to instruct one of our masters the best way to milk us and when we came we had to bellow like a bull. The one who came first got the most points and the one who came last would be punished. They had built strange walls around the room, one on each side, so we faced each other. The wall was about four feet wide, I guess, & went only from our shoulders to above our knees. These walls were between posts holding up a loft. There were large holes cut in the walls at crotch height so our cock & balls would hang through. There were belts with the buckle in front so we could be strapped against the wall and couldn't get away from any torment they wanted to do to our exposed cocks and balls.

While like this, the masters came at us again one at a time & jacked us off again, timing us to see how long it took. We were given ten minutes to rest & we were jacked off again. It took longer the second time. I seemed to come out ok, though not always first but never last. The one poor guy who was last got sucked off by a hungry calf the last afternoon.

My worst came to me the last day we were there. I say worst because I was the only one to get it as I was "different." I am not circumcised and they thought it would be best if I were so I would be more like all the other boys. Struggle as I did I was tied down on the "operating table" with ropes & belts so I couldn't move. They took my hands & tied the balls of one of the boys in one hand and another set in the other. So if I squeezed I would put the poor guys in much pain. The third guy had his hands tied around my balls & was told if he heard either of his fellow initiates holler he was to squeeze my balls. So with that they rolled a table over with all kinds of tools—knives, saws, splicers, clamps, you name it. This I could see but they they put a sheet up in front of me so I couldn't see what they were doing to my cock. They had a terrible argument as to whether it was best to cut the skin off when my cock was hard or soft. Of course it was hard all the time, as it had seemed to be all weekend, so they finally figured it would be better if it were soft so they had to jack me off. You know how sensitive your cock is after you cum? Well the head of mine is like that all the time because the skin always covers it. So after they got through jacking me off they started "cutting." I don't know what they were using but I really thought I would lose it, my cock was so tender, and they were giving it a working over. It wasn't long before I was hard again & they got me to cum twice before I got loose from that table. I was able to keep from squeezing those poor guys' balls so mine were safe too.

OPEN SEASON ON EVERY PLEDGE'S ASS

As if to prove the corporate masculinity of Alpha Chi (not its real name), Hell Week was everything its name implies.

Hell Week began with all pledges being ordered to appear in the game room after dinner wearing only underwear. After forming a straight line, each big brother tied his pledge's wrists behind his back with a length of rope.

As our turns came, we were made to kneel while our heads were shorn bald with a pair of electric clippers. Beards or mustaches were also mercilessly hacked off in spite of any pleas to save them, no matter how impassioned. As soon as our haircuts were completed, our skivvies were stripped off and stuffed in our mouths and were secured by a piece of rag or a long tube sock tied around our heads. Another strip of cloth was used as a blindfold. We were then led downstairs to an unfinished room in the basement where our arms were stretched out and tied to an overhead beam. The next sensation was that of my ankles being kicked none too gently apart and tied to what I later discovered was a wooden bar about three feet wide with pieces of rope threaded through eyelets at both ends. After being spread-eagled in a standing position, naked and totally vulnerable, we were relieved of the remaining hair on our bodies, even the hair on our arms. Most of us on the swim team kept ourselves fairly hairless in an effort to increase our speed in the water. Nevertheless, I was suddenly aware that lather was being applied to my genitals and was warned to stand very still unless I preferred to spend the rest of my life as a eunuch.

Before the evening ended, large black dog collars were fastened around our necks which were to be worn the entire week. In addition to providing a constant source of public humiliation, our collars also proved convenient for leading us around on leashes or tethering us to upright posts or overhead beams. Our hands, when bound behind us, could be elevated out of the way simply by running some extra rope from our wrists to the D-ring in our collars, thereby giving free access to our asses for paddling, or whatever other insidious plans the actives had for us.

Every pledge had a big brother and, prior to Hell Week, a pledge's big brother was mostly the only one to paddle him. The only time the other brothers got in on the act was when a pledge fucked up and had to publicly work off demerits. He did this by providing his ass as a target for the game called "Batter Up." For this he was tied naked over a horse in the fraternity's exercise room. A picture of a baseball, painted on ripstop nylon, was then tied with strings around his waist and legs and centered directly over his ass, providing the target for the bat which was, in reality, a flat paddle cut to resemble a baseball bat. The object was for the poor pledge, whose ass was in the air, not to make any audible sound when struck. A "referee" was always assigned who would rule on whether or not the pledge had emitted so much as a gasp or a whimper. After an accumulation of three "silent" strokes, the referee would yell "You're out!" and the "bat" would pass to the next player. The only good news for the hapless pledge was that he was permitted to shed tears so long as he did so silently, and the strips of Turkish toweling used as blindfolds were usually soaked by the end of a game. Only the risk of extraordinarily severe injury would cause a referee to "call" a game. Needless to say, this diabolical game provided hours of fun for the actives working out in the weight room. However, for the unlucky pledges, it was a horror. It only happened to me twice during the three month pledge period, but both times my ass was in such a hash that even my big brother Eric, who could always find some excuse for putting the wood to my buns, would allow me a few days to recover.

During Hell Week, on the other hand, fraternity tradition decreed that it was open season on every pledge's ass. Even the special clothing we were made to wear encouraged our being beaten. Grey athletic T-shirts which didn't quite reach our navels proclaimed our lowly status in fluorescent orange. On the front was silk-screened the Greek letters of our fraternity, under which, in large bold type, was the word "PLEDGE." On the back was printed "THE BOARD OF EDUCATION MEETS HERE," directly above a big arrow pointing straight down to our buttocks.

Although most of my fellow pledges had been made to wear scratchy burlap in their jockey shorts during at least part of the three month pledge period, special underwear was issued to all the pledges just for Hell Week. Unfortunately, the pledgemaster had seen an advertisement in some sleazy magazine for novelty briefs which were flyless and cut similar to Speedos. They were all-white except for a large black and red bull's-eye printed in the middle of the seat. Also, like Speedos, these briefs were made of nylon tricot, opaque enough to be relatively modest when exposed to public view, yet thin enough not to offer the slightest protection to the poor pledge's ass.

These briefs were worn under a pair of plain white gym shorts, the elastic waist of which facilitated their being easily lowered prior to "assuming the position." Worn with a pair of cowboy boots, which somehow had the uncanny effect of highlighting our hairless legs, our outfits can best be described as embarrassing. It was only the balmy climate of south Texas which permitted the wearing of such skimpy getups in midwinter without freezing our balls off—although I seriously doubt that anyone would have given a shit if we had.

Insult was added to injury in that we were beaten with the paddles we had been forced to make and decorate—all to the fraternity's specifications, of course. In addition, our paddles had to be carried around with us all week and surrendered to any fraternity brother upon demand—anywhere, anytime. Upon handing the paddle to the active, we had to beg for our punishment saying, "Sir, I humbly request that you give me the discipline I need, as you see fit." Upon hearing the order, "Very well pledge, prepare for punishment," we were to respond by yelling, "Sir! Yes Sir!" immediately sliding our gym shorts down to our knees and pulling up our T-shirts so that the back came up over our heads inside out, creating an instant hood. Then, as we bent over grabbing our ankles, the bull's-eye on our asses made a perfect target for the active wielding the paddle. After each resounding splat, we were to announce the count and then say, "Thank you, sir! May I please have another, sir?" What I found especially humiliating about this whole ludicrous ceremony was the thrill it gave the co-eds. It was bad enough to be getting your ass blistered in public wearing only a pair of thin nylon briefs, without having to endure all the mindless girlish giggling.

I spent the entire week ducking from one place to another in a desperate attempt to avoid being intercepted by an active. My luck held until Thursday afternoon, when I had to cross the campus to get to the music school for a piano lesson. Just as I was about to spring up the steps into the safety of the building, I got nailed by one of the two nastiest assholes in the frat who happened to be out for his afternoon run. By the time he had finished with me, I was absolutely in no condition to sit through an hour's lesson on a hard piano bench hammering out Bach, Chopin, Debussy and endless scales and arpeggios.

The expression on my teacher's face as I entered his studio was one of startled incredulity. After looking at my tear stained face, my bald head, my missing mustache, my chafed wrists, the dog collar and the message on my T-shirt, his reaction was one of barely controlled rage. In spite of my protests, he insisted that I slip down both my shorts and my bull's-eye briefs so he could assess the damage to my ass. It was all I could do to talk him out of taking me directly to the Dean of Student Affair's Office to report my fraternity's sadistic treatment of its pledges. He relented only after I explained how pissed off my dad would be if he ever heard that his son was too big a sissy to endure a little hazing.

I cannot ever recall time moving as slowly as it did that week. This was especially true of the time spent in the frat house when we never knew what new horror was about to descend on us.

While in the house during Hell Week, pledges were to be naked except for our bull's-eye briefs and dog collars. At meal times, we served as table waiters for the upperclassmen, after which we ate our food doggy style off dishes on the floor. Anyone caught using his hands immediately had them tied behind him.

The evenings as well as Saturday and Sunday, when not assigned to work details, were largely spent in strenuous physical activities such as games, races and endless physical exercises. Any losing pledge team or individual was usually punished by being made to run a gauntlet of actives wielding paddles.

Another delightful torture, to which we were subjected at least once daily, was to be lined up in a straight line, hands tied behind our backs, with our bull's-eye briefs placed over our heads like hoods. Our big brothers would then position themselves behind us and milk our penises until we shot our semen across the cement floor. The two pledges to shoot either first or farthest would be declared the winners, while the rest would get the paddle. Unfortunately, several of my classmates were almost incapable of getting it up in front of a group of guys; an impediment which brought them considerable grief.

One of the paradoxes of this particular fraternity was its sexuality. Its public image was clearly "super jock" and "super straight," with gays usually being referred to as "those goddam queers." The majority of the guys, including my big brother Eric, were making it with women at least occasionally. Yet, most of the pledges spent a fair amount of time being forced by the actives either to suck their cocks or be fucked by them—usually blindfolded, and often while tied up in one position or another. Occasionally, a dirty sock or a soiled pair of jockey shorts would even be used as a gag.

At the risk of over-psychologizing, this seemingly contradictory phenomenon may not be too surprising considering the activities in which the fraternity was engaging. Perhaps it would be asking too much of the actives not to get turned on sexually while putting naked, hunky young men through such paces as being tied, blindfolded, gagged, shaved and whipped—as well as various forms of vigorous physical activity. This, given the fact that girls were not immediately available for sexual release, may explain part of the homoerotic response on the part of allegedly straight men.

On the other hand, I suppose one might be inclined to dismiss the participation of the pledges by saying that it was simply the price we had to pay if we wished to join the fraternity. However, this could be an over simplification in cases like mine, in which I quickly discovered that along with the humiliation and pain of being paddled and/or tied up, also came powerful sexual stimulation and gratification.

Perhaps, however, I may be forgiven if I tend to be somewhat suspicious of all the macho, queer-bashing bullshit on the part of the actives, and suggest that a lot of these guys had a component in their sexuality they were unwilling to face. I had already come to terms with the fact that I was gay and proud of it, but these guys would be telling you how straight they were while humping your ass or fucking your face. Whatever the cause of this fascinating paradox, the one unwritten rule of the house was that all cocks were *always* to be covered by rubbers prior to insertion in any orifice, male or female and, to facilitate compliance, fish bowls stocked with rubbers were placed in all the bathrooms.

I cannot imagine any of my fellow pledges being happier than I was on the night of our formal initiation into the fraternity. My ass still tingled, my wrists were sore, all my muscles ached and I was completely exhausted. Nevertheless, I had survived! I had also accomplished something which would cause my father to be proud of me. Best of all, even Eric had a slight, if crooked smile on his face as he fastened the pin to my sweater.

CHAINED TO STUDENT UNION RAILING

As pledges at our frat, one night we were ordered to wear jockstraps only and lie on the floor. Our hands were tied in front of us, and then bound to our feet. Each mouth was gagged with a strip of duct tape. They told us to get used to it. Around four a.m. we were roused and had our feet untied. Our other bonds remained intact. They put a pair of ankle cuffs on my feet, connected by a chain, and I have to say the touch of metal against my skin had me moaning like a son of a bitch. Someone had to pull my hair hard to shut me up. All the other pledges had their ankles cuffed. I think a couple of guys were actually more afraid of these "leg irons" than being tied up in the first place.

They loaded us into a van, clanking in the night, destination the student union. We were lined up with our backs against the railing in front of the building. Hands were untied only to be spread and tied down on the railing, as if we were leaning against it. The chains on our feet were chained and locked around the bottom rail. Nobody was running away now. They worked fast, since we were outside, but it was still dark and no one was around. They took some additional lengths of chain and slapped our bodies with them, then each pledge was chained very tightly against the top rail. The chain was wrapped across each back, over the shoulder, across our chests and to the back again, and padlocked at about kidney level. Not only were we tied there, now we were virtually immobilized. Any loosened gags were reinforced with more tape. It was after 6 a.m. and our masters retreated to a safe distance to watch the fun after abusing our bodies and baskets some more.

We were chained to the rail and damned helpless, tied and helpless for nearly four hours before campus security found the tools to cut us free. Not only did the joggers, early risers and guys with early classes give us the once over, getting a hoot out of jockstrapped pledges tied and struggling, but our bare asses could be seen through the open railings. Those who approached the building from the front could see a solid line of butts wiggling nervously and saying good morning in our own clever way.

FRAT
PORTRAITS

🏛

I pledged a fraternity that really believed in male bonding.

I was thrilled to get into my fraternity of choice. At Rush, I met a lot of the actives and was very impressed. The House was over half student jocks and the rest were school senators, class presidents, etc., hunks and studs all.

I was also excited to get in because it was a very athletic house. They won intramurals in several sports and I was very much into sports.

We were told to meet at the fraternity house at 9 pm that night to accept our pledgeship. We were to wear coat and tie as befitting the honor.

We all showed up at 9 pm There were twenty eight of us. We were kept outside for quite a while during which we introduced ourselves to each other. Finally, two of the actives, also dressed in coat and tie, came out of the house, called a name and led that new pledge into the House. This continued every few minutes until finally my name was called.

I was about tenth. My stomach fell when I heard it. The two actives led me into the darkened house for a few feet and stopped. While my eyes were getting accustomed to the dark someone from behind put a blindfold over my eyes.

I jumped, but a couple pairs of hands immediately led me a few feet further and I heard a door close. My coat was taken off of me. A voice told me to sit down and several hands helped me into a chair. The hands remained firmly yet brotherly on my shoulders and upper arms while the voice asked me a couple questions. They dealt mainly with my accepting probational membership into the fraternity.

The hands strongly picked me up and remained on my upper arms as I was escorted out into what seemed to be another room. Here my shirt was unbuttoned. I jumped and tried to stop it but the hands patted me on the shoulder, seeming to say that it was okay. My shirt and t-shirt were taken off, but I could feel that my tie was still on. Again I was told to sit and the hands again helped (read pushed) me into the chair.

Several more questions were asked my by another voice. Again I was picked up off the chair by the hands and led into another room. Here, the hands pushed my hands together behind my back. The next thing I knew, they were tied. I found out later that they used plastic handcuffs, like cops sometimes use.

I was getting a little nervous by now and kind of flinched and tried to struggle some when the hands patted me on the shoulder again and a familiar voice whispered in my ear, "You're okay, don't worry." That calmed me down quite a bit. I recognized that the voice belonged to Harry, a big, muscular, super cool, really hairy guy. I had gotten to know him pretty well during Rush. He later became my big brother.

I was picked up again and taken a few feet, but obviously was out of the room. Someone's arm went around my bare shoulders and Harry's voice whispered, "Don't say anything. Just nod if you're all right." I nodded. He continued, "This is just part of the ceremony. Stay calm, be quiet, and just do as you're told, for John, for Brent, and for me. Okay?" I nodded again.

John and his roommate Brent lived across the hall from me in the dorms. They were both actives and we had gotten to be good friends. It was they who had gotten me to go to the Rush party.

Hands again took hold of me and led me down some steps. I still had my hands tied behind me and I was still blindfolded. Suddenly a door closed behind me. I could hear several muffled noises and some shuffling. Finally, someone said, "Who is it?" I gave my name. It was the other pledges. We were all blindfolded and tied.

Every several minutes after that another pledge was brought in. When we started making too much noise talking, somebody would come in and tell us to keep it down. Finally, they came and took Craig out. When he came back all we could understand was "MMMMMMM." We supposed they gagged him. After that we were much quieter.

After what seemed like hours, the actives came and took the whole lot of us back upstairs. Our hands were kept tied but our blindfolds came off. I felt Harry's familiar hands on my shoulders again.

The room was dark, except for the candles that each active was holding. They were all standing shirtless, with black executioner-like hoods, black pants and the fraternity initials painted on their chests. There must have been fifty or more incredible looking, well built studs there.

We were brought to the front one by one and presented before the group, where we were formally asked if we wanted to be part of the fraternity. After our agreement, our neckties were taken off of us and a big "P" was painted on our chests.

We were led back into the basement where we stayed for

quite a while, blindfolded. Finally Rick, the chapter president, Brent and a couple other actives came after us and took the blindfolds off, but left the plastic handcuffs on. We went upstairs and had our first pledge meeting.

Rick introduced Brent as the Pledge Master and explained his duties. He also introduced Chip as the Assistant Pledge Master. Brent took over the meeting from there and explained a lot of stuff about pledging. We had to wear small pledge pins at all times, even when naked. He also told us about "rides." I remember I got excited just hearing it described.

Being taken on a ride basically meant being kidnapped. Generally a pledge would be tied up and dropped off somewhere. But there *were* rules.

At least two pledges had to be taken at the same time. The purpose of rides was to promote pledge unity. What better way to get unified than to struggle together against an obstacle.

At least one of the pledges had to have some kind of clothes on.

A pledge couldn't be taken for a ride after 12 midnight on week nights or 2 am on weekends.

The pledges had to have a quarter on them for a phone call. A pledge could get out of a ride by challenging the active. That meant challenging him to quiz the pledge on the information related to the fraternity. If the pledge got all the questions right the active had to let him go. Pledges could do the same to actives.

We elected Craig as the pledge class president, did a few other items of business and were escorted home. We were still tied and were blindfolded before leaving the house. When I got back to the dorm, still tied and blindfolded, John was there to give me a hard time. He put me in my room and gagged me by putting a couple lengths of athletic tape over my mouth and around my head. It was a while before my roommate came and got me loose.

It had been a long night and I couldn't wait for my pledgeship to begin!

JOHN

John, the active who lived across the hall from me, was incredible looking, about 6'4", 240 lbs., with no body fat. He was on the football and powerlifting teams. He had been an all state wrestler in high school. He usually walked around the dorm completely naked and was he ever hung—I'd say he was about ten thick inches at rest! He was very cocky—with good reason—but was really a good guy.

John set himself a yearly goal of taking every pledge on a ride single handed and at the same time not getting taken on a ride himself. He was always involved in pledge hazing, especially when it came to bondage. In fact, he was usually the instigator and the one with the ideas.

When he decided it was your turn to be taken on a ride by him, he would come into your room dressed only in a jock and carrying two rolls of athletic tape. One roll had written on it: "For use on John." On the other roll were the words, "For use on…" with your name on it. Then he would tell you to strip to a jock, also.

He did bring a couple of the actives with him. He said they were only observers, to make sure the match was fair. Not that he needed their help against me.

He outweighed me by about 75 lbs. of solid muscle, so it took him all of five minutes to have me tied and gagged completely.

He had my wrists taped behind me and also my upper arms. My ankles were taped together as were my knees. He took off his jock and stuffed it in my mouth and taped it over. His jock had a strong taste. He ripped my jock off of me and tied off my dick and balls, taking great care to separate and stretch them.

As a final touch, he turned me on my stomach and wrote something in magic marker on my ass. I found out later that he'd written, "Artwork by JOHN." He also put the fraternity initials on my chest. He let me lie there for a while to catch my breath while he went to his room and put on some shorts.

When he came back, he picked me up and threw me over his shoulder, crushing my bound balls into his hard chest and shoulder. The other actives said they'd see him at the House. I guessed that was my next destination.

When we got to the car, he asked me if I was okay. He said he hoped I knew he wasn't doing this because he didn't like me. On the contrary, he said, he usually did his best work on guys that he really liked, and that he really liked me. He listed a bunch of things that he liked about me. It was really quite touching. I felt like I had made a lasting friend. (I had. John and I became such good friends that I was his favorite victim and he regularly got me even after I became an active).

He checked my bonds and the gag, then took me over to the fraternity house. He got out of the car, went to the trunk and brought a long hank of rope, with which he tied me securely to his bucket seat, tying the rope around my chest several times. "That should hold you till I get back," he said, and went into the house.

I tried the best I could to get free and was starting to get my wrists loose when he came out, with someone else over his shoulder.

It was Chris, one of my pledge brothers. He was tied much the same way I was. John put him in the back seat, came around the car, took off the rope from around my chest and checked my wrists. "Not bad, but not quick enough." He put several more rounds of tape around my wrists and slapped me on the chest. "Let's go."

We drove for a few minutes when he suddenly pulled the car over to the curb. We were in a bad section of town and I didn't want to be dropped off here. He looked at me and smiled and gave me a wink. "Don't want to make this too easy, do we?"

He got out of the car and walked around to my side, opened the door and started to lift me out. My heart sank. I did not want to be left in a bad part of town, tied, gagged and naked.

Instead, he blindfolded me and Chris with a strip of towel, got back in the car and drove off. "Relieved?" he asked. He drove for quite a while, then finally stopped the car, picked me up and set me down on what felt (to my naked butt) like some twigs and grass. I heard the car drive away.

I struggled for a few minutes and got the blindfold off. Chris was sitting right in front of me. Even with his arms tied behind him, I could tell they were huge. He was on the wrestling team and I could imagine the wrestling match that he and John must have had to get him in a position like this.

His cock and balls looked like they were tied similar to mine and he had a huge hard on, like mine.

We finally helped each other get free, even though it took quite a while. Chris had twenty-five cents taped to his chest for a phone call, but we ended up walking all the way back to the dorm all the same. We never did pass a phone on the way.

John was in my room watching TV when I got back. He looked at his watch and said, "Not bad, not a record, but not bad. Do you want to try for two out of three?" He laughed, slapped my butt and went over to his room.

PLEDGE PRESENTATION

It was only about 6 pm when I heard a knock on the door. I didn't even think about not opening it; the actives' pranks and hazing never started until after 9 pm and besides, there was a meeting for the actives tonight at 7:30. Nothing would happen before then, but watch out after that, I thought. But for some reason, I still had an uneasy feeling.

When I opened the door, John and Brent were standing there.

"Could you come to the fraternity house with us for a while? We're supposed to do a presentation for the meeting tonight and we need your help." I had long ago learned that you don't say no to a fraternity brother, so I went with them.

When we got over to the house Brent and I went into the meeting room and John went in the back. I asked Brent what I needed to do. He led me over to the fireplace and told me to stand on the raised hearth. Suddenly John rushed out and he and Brent started tying me up!

I struggled but it didn't do a whole lot of good. John outweighed me by 75 lbs. Brent was no weakling, either. He only outweighed me by about 25 lbs., but he definitely knew what he was doing.

My hands were stretched and tied to bolts that were anchored to the exposed beams in the ceiling. John pulled a knife from his pocket and cut my T-shirt off of me. He balled some of it up and stuffed it in my mouth and used some more of it to tie it around my head.

As I moaned, John and Brent undid my belt buckle, unbuttoned my fly and pulled off my jeans. I was wearing white briefs, which they quickly disposed of as well.

Brent took one foot and John took the other and tied them to bolts in the floor, stretching me out like a capital "X." Brent took a large magic marker out of his pocket and drew the fraternity initials on my chest, while John took some rope and tied it to my dick and balls in a figure eight fashion. He played with me and massaged me as he did it. He pulled out some tit clamps on a chain and attached them tightly to my nipples. I let out a moan.

He took the nipple chain and tied it to the rope around my balls and tied that to another rope that stretched clear across the meeting room and ran across the floor.

Brent blindfolded me with some more of my t-shirt and they left me there. I figured out that I was the presentation they were talking about needing to make for the meeting.

I hung there for quite a while before I heard any noise. Of course, when you are tied and blindfolded, it is hard to tell how long has passed. Especially, tied like that, each moment seems like hours.

I heard some giggling and laughing and some moving of chairs and some talking. Someone said, "John really outdid himself this time." Finally, Richard the fraternity president opened the meeting. After welcoming everyone he said, "We'd really like to thank John and Brent for our centerpiece this evening."

Right then I felt a hard pull on my cock and nipples and let out a moan. The actives laughed hysterically.

Richard then made a comment about how well trained the pledges were this year. Again, I felt the pull and moaned. During the next several minutes I was the trained seal act, moaning every time someone pulled on the rope. They did several things of business and I moaned with each vote, my moan depending on the preference of the guy at the other end of the rope.

Finally, Richard said it was time to clear out the scum so they could have the heart of their meeting. I felt myself being cut down only to have my hands tied tightly behind me. I was carried by several more hands into the basement, and put in a chair, where I was tied more securely.

I think it was John again doing the tying, his favorite activity. My feet were tied to the legs of the chair and a rope was tied from my still bound hands to my still bound balls. Every time I tried to pull on my hands, I pulled on my nuts.

I was there for what seemed like forever. I knew that it wouldn't do a lot of good to get loose, they would all just come after me. I did spend the time fantasizing what would happen next.

I finally heard some noises come down the steps. Suddenly, the ropes around my wrists were cut and the blindfold came off. It was John and Brent. They cut me loose and said that I had done such a good job that they were going to take me out for a beer.

I thought it was another prank, but that's what happened. John and Brent had gotten some kind of award for most original pledge presentation, so they were in very good moods. All in all it was a great evening for all of us.

DAVE

Dave had a lot going for him. He was a sexy guy, about 6', 180 lbs., with dark brown hair, steel blue eyes and an athletic build. And he was rich. His parents gave him a BMW for graduating high school. Girls were all over him constantly.

When he came back to school after his sophomore year, he had gotten really cocky. I guess everything just finally went to his head.

I was pledging that year and all I knew about Dave was that he gave the pledges a really hard time. That is until the actives got tired of his attitude.

One Friday night we were at the fraternity house. A few actives (including Dave) were getting their rocks off by hazing a couple of pledges who were there. It was after 1 am.

All of a sudden the doors burst open and about fifteen guys rushed in. They were wearing black executioner-style hoods and the fraternity initials were painted on their bared chests. Several of them were carrying rope and athletic tape. I was sure they were after us. I think Dave thought that too.

All of a sudden they jumped Dave. He was loosely tied with the rope and carried outside. One of the actives told me to come along to see what would happen if I ever got a bad attitude. We all jumped in a couple of cars and Dave was thrown into the trunk. We ended up at the girls' dorm.

Dunham Hall was three stories tall and had a courtyard right in the middle. It was a very pretty area with flowers, a brick walkway and smack in the middle, surrounded by flowers were three Roman columns, made to look like they were antiques brought over from Italy.

All fifteen guys opened the trunk. Dave had already gotten

loose and was swearing and fighting when the whole group picked him up. He was carried through the big iron gates leading to the courtyard and taken over to the middle column. He was making so much noise I could see girls peeking out from their windows to see what was going on.

Dave was stripped down to his skimpy black briefs and tied to the pillar, yelling and swearing the whole time. First his wrists were brought around to the back of the pillar and tied, then his arms and ankles and upper thighs. Several lengths of rope were brought around his chest. The group obviously knew what it was doing. They moved strong and fast. I knew that they had plenty of experience in it from taking pledges on so many rides.

After he was securely tied, John, the biggest and most muscular active went over to him and asked if he knew why his own brothers were doing this to him. He yelled, "Fuck you!" a couple times and John blindfolded him, and said they were going to leave him there for a while to think about it.

As Dave yelled "Fuck you!" a couple more times, John and a couple of the other guys forced a gag down his throat and tied it around his head.

John whispered something in Dave's ear and Dave dropped his head and nodded. I couldn't hear it but it seemed like Dave's attitude changed from then on.

Some of the brothers looked in my direction and said that I would have to cut the briefs off of him. They said that brothers shouldn't do that to other brothers, but since I was a pledge, I could.

John went up with me and stuck the blade in the front leg of the briefs. He carefully and playfully put it to Dave's member and moved it around. Dave moaned and shook his head. John took my hand and placed it on the knife handle and showed me how to pull up.

I did and the knife cut easily up to the waist band where I had a little trouble. The briefs partially fell off, showing some pubes. I did the same thing to the other side.

His dick fell out. It was thick, semi-hard and long.

John handed me a narrow leather strap with a small lock. I had never seen anything like that and looked at him puzzled. He whispered that I was supposed to put it on Dave around his cock and balls and lock it on.

As I locked it on, several of the actives formed a line and each whispered something in Dave's ear. Each time his head dropped a little more and he nodded. When they finished, I was sure I saw a couple tears on his cheeks.

They checked his bonds, then grabbed me and asked me what right a lowly scum pledge like me had in doing something like that to an active. I was grabbed and thrown into the trunk. I wondered if I would get the same treatment as Dave, but no such luck.

I snuck back over to see Dave later that night. He was still tied to the column, struggling. I took some pictures and hid in some bushes almost all night looking at him. I also took videos.

About 4 am or so a campus security guard came by and saw Dave. He took off the blindfold and stared at him for a couple of minutes, examining him closely. Then he took the gag out.

"What the hell are you doing here like that," he said.

Dave immediately started yelling something like, "What the fuck do you think, you fucking asshole, that I did this to myself?!!!" He kept it up for several minutes after which the campus cop walked around him like he was going to untie him.

He circled several times and Dave said, "What the fuck are you waiting for, you shithead? Untie me!!!"

I guess the cop didn't like that so he walked around front, gave Dave a hard double tittie twister and when Dave yelled, "Ouch!" he stuck the gag back in Dave's mouth and secured it in. Then he walked around and made sure he was tied tight and left.

I was shocked and so was Dave, who started struggling fiercely now. It didn't do him any good, though.

I finally got enough nerve to go over to him. He jumped when I lightly ran my fingers down him and played with his nipples some. He moaned several times, but not in anger, but I was really nervous and ran back into the bushes quickly.

About 5:30 or 6, John showed up. He took the blindfold off and quietly talked to Dave for a while. I strained but couldn't hear what he was saying. Dave nodded several times and looked like he was crying again. Finally John walked around and cut him loose.

Dave gave John a big hug. I could hear his sobbing. Then they walked out the big iron gate. I stayed in my hiding place for a while longer, then went home.

The next night there was a knock on my door. I opened it and there stood Dave. I got scared that it was time for his revenge and tried to close the door. He stopped the door and said that he wasn't there to do anything to me. He said that he just wanted to talk.

I let him in feeling like he was lying, but realized that I would get gotten eventually anyway. No one else was with him though. That seemed odd. There was no way he could take me by himself.

I sat on the bed and he sat next to me. He said that he heard that I was the one who cut off his briefs and locked the strap around his cock and balls. He apologized for his attitude of the past and said that he really wasn't a jerk. He was going to be at the next pledge meeting to apologize to all of us too. He was also going to apologize to the actives at their meeting.

I asked him about the strap and he said that it was still locked on. He said that the year he became an active, one of the guys had his locked on for a couple months. He said that the way he had been treating everyone that he guessed that would happen to him, too. He also told me that I would be one of the first to know. There was a tradition that whoever put it on, took it off, and that I would have some input as to when that was, even though I was just a pledge.

He then said that it wouldn't make a difference to my pledge status and he did plan to get his revenge, but it would be in fun, not in jerkiness.

We got to be good friends after that and he did get his revenge often, but the pledges and I got him a couple times, all in good fun. I did get to take the strap off a couple weeks later, too.

UNTAPING CRAIG

Craig was our pledge class president. He was blond and built. Because of his size he got hazed a little more than the rest of us. It was like he was a challenge or something.

One night at about 2 am as I was soundly sleeping, the phone rang. It was Randy, Craig's roommate. "You'd better get over here right away."

I jumped into some clothes and went to his room. When

Randy opened the door, I saw a big glob of athletic tape lying on the bed. It was moaning. On closer look, I realized that it was Craig.

The only body parts that weren't covered with tape were his nose, his nipples, and the top of his head.

Randy and I teased him for a second or two, but we could tell that he wasn't in his usual good humor, so we started freeing him. I was going to cut the gag off, but Randy told me not to, that he would probably scream when we ripped off the rest of the tape and that would keep him a little quiet.

We apologized for the pain that we were about to cause, but told him that there was no other way to get him loose.

We cut the tape off from around his eyes and had to cut quite a bit of hair just to do that. We did his chest, playing with his nipples all the while. We pulled off just about all of his fine, blond, chest hair while doing that.

Next we decided to undo his crotch. Tears were running down his face as we pulled on his pubes. The actives had taken great care to tape his balls and dick and put several layers on. I took my time and made sure to squeeze a few times. It was kind of funny to see all those curly hairs all over the discarded tape.

We did his legs after that, saving his arms and hands for last. We let him undo the gag himself. When he was finally free, he lay on the bed sweating for a long time. He didn't say anything for several minutes. He just lay there, breathing hard and sweating.

When he finally did talk, he told us what had happened. He told us that at about 11 pm, right after he had gotten out of the shower, there was a knock on the door. When he opened it, eight or nine actives jumped in and tackled him. All he had on was a towel.

One of the actives said, "Look what an opportunity we have here," and the tape started flying.

After they had his wrists, elbows, knees and ankles taped and he was gagged, he assumed they were finished and thought he'd be taken out somewhere and dropped off. However, he was really surprised when one of the brothers said that they couldn't quit now and started giving him a hand job while the others held him down. He was moaning and trying to get the guy off of him to no avail.

Just as he relaxed and started to get excited, the active pulled out the tape and started taping his nuts and dick. All he could do was moan. The active took several lengths from Craig's cock and taped it under his butt and up up his crack to his wrists. This was done several times.

They went ahead and mummified him after that, leaving his eyes and his nipples exposed. One of his brothers played with his nipples quite a bit and he could feel himself getting very turned on. Then they blindfolded him. He'd been there ever since, unable to move or do anything except plan revenge on the entire brotherhood of the fraternity.

CEREMONY

As part of our initiation we had to make paddles for our big brothers.

We the pledges were told that there was to be a kind of informal ceremony where we pledges presented our big brothers with our fraternity paddles. As we got to the house we were led into the basement and told to strip down to our jocks and to hang the paddles around our necks. (When we made the

HAZING

paddles, we had to have a hole drilled into the base of the handle with a long leather cord put through it).

A few minutes later our big brothers came down and talked to us. Mine told me that the ceremony was a time for him and me to bond as brothers and he was really happy to have the opportunity to share it with me. He told me that part of the ceremony was to learn trust in a big brother. He said that the next part was symbolic and told me to put my hands together in front of me.

I did as I was told. Then he handcuffed me with the plastic cuffs that cops use on TV when there is a riot or something. He also blindfolded me with a disk blindfold and led me up the stairs with his arm over my shoulder.

At the top of the stairs he said that he would have to gag me. He said that it was symbolic of the fact that as brothers I would never reveal the secrets of the fraternity. I opened my mouth and he put a plug in my mouth and strapped it tightly around my head.

As pledges we had been tied and gagged many times, but before, it was always with rope and athletic tape, or maybe socks and jocks as gags. This seemed like a real ceremony.

I stayed there for what seemed like several minutes, thinking I heard low noises and little giggles. Then my blindfold was taken off. In the dim light I could see the fraternity brothers, all with their shirts off standing in a double line, facing each other, with an aisle between the lines. They were wearing black executioner style hoods and had the fraternity initials painted on their chests.

The pledgemaster came from behind me and led one of the pledges to the line, and took him to his big brother. He did that to each of us. With big ceremony the president of the fraternity stood in front of the group in an executioner's hood and said a few words.

On cue, our big brothers took the paddles from around our necks and led us back to the wall. The pledgemaster and a couple of the other actives forced each of us on all fours on the floor and told us that we had to crawl the line. I was about fifth in line and my face was pushed into the naked butt of my pledge brother as we crawled slowly (our hands were cuffed in front of us). I could feel breathing on my butt so I'm sure that someone was right behind me too.

We stopped and I couldn't see anything in front of me except a crack and a butt, but I could hear whacks, laughs and muffled moans. I was scared.

My brother in front finally took off and I could see clearly. The whacks seemed hard and fast. There were probably about twenty or more guys on each side. As soon as my brother got about half way through the line I was pushed forward. I tried going as fast as I could, but the whacks smarted like hell.

I was made to keep crawling until my nose was pushed into my pledgebrother's ass again. This time his was cherry red and I'm sure mine was too. I heard a few whimpers through the gags of my fellow pledges. I thought I was going to cry but was determined not to.

We were brought to our feet again. We were blindfolded and led back down into the basement. I stood there for a while and my hands were forced over my head and hooked onto something. My legs were forced apart and tied to the pledge's legs beside me. I was on tiptoe.

We stayed there for what seemed like forever. My butt was

burning big time. I knew that I wouldn't be able to sit for a while and was wondering if you could get blisters from a spanking.

Right about then I heard a thud and a moan. Then there was another thud and another moan. I knew what it was. The spanking was starting again. Then I got hit, hard.

I guess that everyone got one hit and then the hitting started with everyone. The guy spanking me, my big brother, wasn't doing it too hard, but plenty hard enough for me to feel it, especially after the beating I had just gone through.

In a few minutes it was over. Then the ice started. It was rubbed all over my sore ass and actually felt really good until it was put down the pouch of my jock. I could feel something being drawn on my ass, then the blindfold came off and I saw my big brother standing in front of me.

He smiled and said that it was over and asked me if I was okay. He unhooked my arms but my legs were still tied to my friend's beside me. The guy on one side was cut free from me. I was blindfolded again. The two of us were still tied side by side and we were led outside.

We walked around for quite a while before we finally stopped. My jock was pulled down around my ankles and athletic tape was wrapped around my upper body several times so I couldn't bring my arms up to the gag or blindfold.

We were there for what seemed like a long time, maybe ten or fifteen minutes. (Believe me, that is a long time when you are tied, gagged, blindfolded, naked, and have no idea where you are).

Finally I heard some noises of people laughing. My blindfold was taken off and I was in the lounge in my dorm with a lot of my dormmates around me.

The guy who lived next door cut our legs free, took the jock from around my ankles, put it over my head and led me up to my dorm room and sat me on the bed. He said that he'd be right back. I was hoping that he would get something to free me, instead he brought a camera.

He stood me up and blindfolded me again and snapped several pictures. Then I heard the door close. He left.

I finally made it over to my bed where I sat for an hour or more until my roommate came in. I was about believing that he was going to pull an all nighter and never come home.

He laughed for a long time, made a few rude and crude comments, said that my ass was bright red, and laid me on my bed and told me good-night.

I didn't want to stay like that all night and started moaning and thrashing frantically. He finally cut me free, laughing all the time.

I went to the mirror and looked at my super, bright red ass. My big brother had signed his name there. I didn't care. Just thinking about trying to scrub it off hurt.

TICKLED BY MAX

🏛

I was about halfway through the pledge period. One night I was in my room studying. There was a knock at the door and before I could do anything, it burst open. Seven guys came in and jumped me. I was dressed in my usual dorm attire, gym shorts, nothing else.

Even though I put up a great fight, I was stripped, which was a favorite thing for the actives to do to me. I am pretty well hung with more than adequate balls and I'm uncut. They liked to tease me about it when I couldn't do or say anything.

They'd always go for the feet first, tying them with athletic tape. Then they'd go for the wrists, behind the back. Then they'd usually tape the knees, then the upper arms. Finally, they'd stuff a rag, a sock or something in my mouth and secure it with a few layers of athletic tape. Even with my size and strength, with seven guys the whole thing only took a few minutes.

They put me ass up on the bed and each guy signed his name to my butt, in magic marker. Then they turned me over and wrote the fraternity name on my chest. As usual, they made some rude and crude comments about my dick and ball size and about my uncutness.

Then they all left, but Max, who stayed behind to keep an eye on me and to make sure I couldn't escape. After I lay there for a few minutes, he checked my bonds. He sat me up and tightly put a couple runs of rope around my chest and arms. I grimaced a little because it tickled. Big mistake on my part. He noticed it right away.

Max started slowly and lightly running his fingers up and down me. I was squirming and wriggling, unable to laugh through the gag. He enjoyed seeing that and started going at it more in earnest.

He'd circle my nipples and go down to my abs and belly button, then down to my pube area. I was bouncing up and down on the bed, letting out muffled laughter through the gag. I was getting worried that I couldn't get enough air through the gag, when he stopped. He was laughing, too.

He got some leftover rope and tied my taped ankles to the foot of the bed. He wrapped a couple lengths of rope around me and under the bed. I couldn't move. I was extremely uncomfortable from lying on my hands, but was happy to get some air.

He stopped again. I looked down and saw beads of sweat all over my chest and my dick was sticking straight up. It was the biggest hard on I had ever had.

He started at it again and my hips started bucking some involuntarily. He took a short piece of rope and tied it around my dick and balls, mainly so he could show my hard on to the other guys. Then he patted me on the chest and said, "Not tonight, brother."

I remember that I was really surprised that he called me brother. That was something an active never called a pledge.

About that time the other guys came in with Curt, my pledge brother. He was tied and gagged the same way I was but was wearing briefs which they pulled down to compare us. They all laughed about my erection and Max demonstrated my ticklishness. Finally, I was untied from the bed and taken with Curt out to the woods away from campus.

It took a few hours, but we finally got undone. I got free before Curt and jacked off before letting him loose. Then I took off his briefs and put them on. I left his hands tied for a while so he wouldn't try to get his briefs back.

PLEDGES
AS MARINES

🏛

My frat's Hell Week was a little different. You see, we had a theme. Hell Week was designed to resemble somebody's idea of a marine boot camp, right down to forced marches, iron bunks and the olive drab underwear we had to wear. There was no way to hide your underwear because we had to strip down to the undershirt and shorts as soon as we gained permission to enter the house. Orders were barked out and you had to answer with a loud "Yes SIR!" or "No SIR!" It was a true exercise in total humiliation. Besides forced pushups and situps, forced mindless chores like cleaning toilets with toothbrushes, and forced marches around the house property in broad daylight dressed in that damn underwear, we had to endure surprise inspections. The Pledgemasters stomped into the basement where we pledgemaggots were bunking for the week. As soon as they entered, we had to jump to attention, chests out, stomachs in, bare feet together. We'd get a lecture about what fucks we were. If a Master yelled "Inspec-SHUN!" we had to snap to at ease position, legs apart except we had to clasp our hands tight behind our heads. While some actives tore through our stuff, others patted us down, more of a grabass grope than a frisk, as if we had concealed weapons. All we wore was that olive drab underwear, so where could we hide stuff? In our hair? Up our asses?

If a rule was violated, say if they found something out of place during Inspection or if a dude forgot his place or didn't stand straight enough, we were punished first by being handcuffed. Being young and dumb at the time, I thought you had to be a cop or a detective to own handcuffs, but the actives had pairs in spades. That made it seem all the more exotic, erotic, even dangerous to have your wrists cuffed behind you.

A pledge who broke a rule was immediately cuffed and led away to the Discipline Quarters, home of the Pipe and the Paddle. I know because I visited there three times, and all three times it was about the same. I was cuffed and marched away to a room just off the kitchen with some exposed pipes hanging near the ceiling, sort of an old boiler room being put to different use. The Pledgemaster forced a couple of rags down my throat and tied another around it, then unlocked the cuffs. Before I could go AWOL, which was a pointless exercise I'll explain later, a couple of actives stripped me bare butt naked and my wrists were cuffed around a sturdy metal pipe over my head. The heights of the overhead pipe and yours truly were just enough that I had to raise myself on my toes to keep in contact with the cold floor. Once my feet were tied together, the other times they weren't. By this time, my sex drive was churning away and I moaned and mumbled my helpless pleasure in spite of myself, which sounded like pleas for help through the gag and got a laugh from the Pledgemaster. I think everybody's cocks got harder in that situation, even those of the marine macho actives, so no one paid much attention to a stiff prick beyond acknowledging its presence and laughing at the size of it.

The pledge paddles were big mothers, sturdy pine jobs stained deep brown and lacquered smooth until they positively gleamed in the right light. In the center there were three holes the size of dimes in a triangular shape, for the Greek letter delta. A Pledgemaster would recite the charges as I put up a weak but erotic struggle, as if I could break the cuffs like Houdini and still escape somehow. The actives would decide how many blows your violation deserved, always too many. You'd tense your body, clench your butt, and wait for the inevitable. You knew what was coming, but the first blow always took me by surprise. I'd have jumped three feet but I was tied up at the time. You barely had time to get over the sting when the next blow struck your butt. They didn't linger over paddling, the idea was to inflict as much pain as fast as possible. Although I was tied up, I was agile enough to wiggle or hop out of perfect paddling position, so an Active, shirtless and mean-looking, clamped his hands on my shoulders to keep me still. One hand traveled all the way down to my balls and cock. He took hold and squeezed them like a garlic press, looking me straight in the eye and daring me to do anything about it, while the Pledgemaster or his Aide paddled harder. Now I was getting it from both ends. I've never believed in noble suffering of torture with stoic, macho silence. Half the fun is being made to give in and scream your fucking head off. Even with the gag, people must've heard me in forty-six states when that dude manhandled my cock.

I stayed cuffed and gagged long enough for all the upperclassmen who hadn't been on Discipline Patrol to get a good look and feel at me. My hands were then cuffed behind my back and I was escorted naked back to our bunks, in front of all the other pledges, with a red, red behind proving that I'd been punished for my sins. Face down on the bunk, so everyone could get a good look at my sore butt and tremble I guess, my arms were spread to the corners and each wrist was cuffed to a rung on the post. My ankles were spread and tied to the foot of the bed. I did my penance, in plain view of everyone. Some nights there'd be three or four guys in the same position. You can't move much when you're tied like that, but I managed to wriggle my crotch enough to rub my cock against the sheets in a no hands jerk off.

Like I said, no pledge could leave without permission, and during drilling and training sessions there was no permission to be had. But a fellow pledge broke rank and slipped away to quaff a few with some friends. Maybe he forgot that we had a pledge class that night or maybe he didn't care. When he strolled in, thinking he'd gotten away with it, he was dragged to the lounge and stripped when he didn't get naked fast enough. They bent him over a chair and he had his butt paddled while two guys held him down. He got twenty strokes, yelling like crazy after the first ten. His hands were forced behind him and cuffed, then he was gagged with duct tape and his feet were tied together with rope, all while he was bent over that chair. The Pledgemaster tied a rope around his neck and led him to the Discipline Quarters. He had to hop like a puppet because of his bound feet, and the rest of the pledges were ordered to follow everyone else to Discipline.

Discipline Quarters weren't very large, but those who didn't squeeze in had a good view through the door from the kitchen. The Pledgemaster made sure all pledges, properly attired in our tight olive drab shorts and no shirts, were up front to see and be seen. The AWOL pledge's wrists were handcuffed to the overhead pipe.

The Pledgemaster said it was our fault our brother pledge had bolted without leave, so we all had to "share his shame." The frat officers pulled out a cacophony of handcuffs and all pledges had their hands cuffed in back. One pledge talked back and had his mouth taped by an officer who promised to wash out his mouth with soap, and did, later. The AWOL pledge received his second paddling in less than twenty minutes, in bondage this time. By the time the Pledgemaster finished, the AWOL pledge was almost hanging limp from the pipe. He was taken down, and all of us spent that night chained face up to our bunks, gagged with tape and struggling quietly.

Because the AWOL pledge had brought us to that torture, we did our best to make his life a living hell to make sure he didn't sneak out again, and the Pledgemaster encouraged it. We found novel ways to cement his bonds to the House, tying him with undershirts, gagging him with his underwear or socks, even giving him a spanking and keeping him bare butt naked all the time. Working to keep him tied up actually brought the rest of us closer together! We were only as strong as our weakest link, as the cliche goes.

HELL WEEK EVE

After one and a half semesters of being treated like slaves and robots, hell week was a riot, but the best part took place on hell week-eve.

When the pledges arrived for dinner on the Friday night before hell week began, we knew something was up by the looks and smirks we were getting. After serving dinner and being made to feel like shit, as usual, we sat at our lowly table and prepared to eat, when all the pledges were grabbed and quickly tied to our chairs. Our hands were roped behind our backs and tied to the chair, our feet tied together, and we were blindfolded with black cloths. Roped in place and good and helpless, we knew hell week was beginning a little early. To chants of "GO-GO-GO!" we were "fed dinner by hand." Unseen hands smeared food and other crap down our throats, and all over our faces and clothes. Our dinner was not the roast beef we'd served the others. We got peanut butter and jelly, raw eggs and vodka. My dazed efforts to loosen the knots on my wrists got me nowhere.

After our adventure in fine dining, the blindfolds were removed from our eyes and were used to gag our mouths, tight and effective. We looked like hell, fifteen of us covered with food and assorted shit, struggling and silenced in our ropes and gags.

Snyder, an ominous and hunky junior who looked like a young Mephistopheles at that moment, told us to sit quietly and think about the tortures we would have to endure in the days to come. We moaned and pulled on the damned ropes, but our compliance seemed assured.

The frat's officers sucked down a couple of beers and looked in on us for awhile, occasionally pulling on our hair and checking the knots. One of them planted his foot on my thigh, lifted my head by my hair, and decided my gag was too loose. "Got to keep you nice and quiet. This isn't in there tight enough, is it, fuckface?" he said as he took out the gag. "Answer, pledge!" "Sir, Yes Sir! Sir, Thank You, Sir!" I roared back in my best submissive/macho voice, and then he rammed the cloth in my mouth and tied it behind my head. "I oughta put my socks in there, fuckhead," and he reached down to snap his socks, but he didn't carry out that threat.

After 20 minutes, or thereabouts, the officers got bored and sought other diversions. We wrestled with the ropes and gags. A husky blond dude named Joel twisted and grunted and managed to get his hands undone. In triumph, he bent to untie his feet and tore off the gag, while the rest of us pleaded with our eyes. Joel laughed and started untying his friend, Danny, when Snyder and a couple others walked in. You might say they weren't pleased to see Joel unbound. Snyder held Joel's arms while the guys finished untying Danny's ankles. They dragged them away, Danny still gagged, and promised punishment, leaving the rest of us bound and gagged and scared, but relieved that Joel hadn't tried to free us after all. It also made us stop struggling so hard to undo the ropes.

I could hear loud noises and laughter coming from somewhere else in the house, accompanied by Joel's voice screaming "SIR, YES SIR!" a number of times. Pushups were the favorite house punishment, and I figured my two fellow pledges were doing a million or so as penance, until we heard the unmistakable "SWOP!" of a paddle on bare skin.

Thirty more minutes passed, with no word on the fates of Joel and Danny. Our wardens marched in and untied our hands and feet. They ordered us not to try to remove the gags as we were hustled into the front lounge. Joel and Danny were already there, still in bondage, still gagged, with their arms stretched over their heads and their wrists bound to the staircase railing. Their feet were on the floor, but just barely. Their shirts were off, and their pants and underwear were in clumps around their ankles. Joel and Danny had been strung up facing the staircase, and their backsides revealed reddened evidence of a thorough butt paddling. Both of them got a few more strokes as we watched and got a "this can happen to you, assholes" speech. We had to grunt our "Sir, Yes Sirs" through our gags until it was loud enough to satisfy Snyder.

We groaned as our hands were tied behind us again, and we got our orders for the next day. Instead of being strung up like our naked fellow pledges, we were booted out of the front door and into the quadrangle! I looked back and saw Joel and Danny watch us leave, like their last hope of rescue had been foiled.

We were able to walk, but our hands and mouths were tied, and the whole world seemed to be watching. Since the house was full, most of us pledges were still in dorms, and we had to make our ways home all tied up. Walking across campus was embarrassing, but it was a little like wearing a proud badge of servitude, or at least that's what I kept telling myself. It was even more embarrassing to stand by the dorm's security door and sheepishly wait for someone to untie us or at least open the door for us, since our bound hands couldn't reach our keys. People were laughing themselves shitless at our plight. The door finally opened and I ran upstairs to my room, and kicked at the door. But my asshole roommate was out!

I sank to the corridor floor and tried to wriggle and writhe out of the ropes. My next door neighbor heard me cussing into the gag and had a good laugh. He took off the gag and I screamed, "Untie me, asshole!" Then he gagged me again! And he teased me until I nodded agreement to his demand to buy him a month's supply of beers. He reached into my pocked and fished for the keys.

The rest of hell week had its share of humiliation and domination, but there was no more bondage to speak of, unless you count the time when I was forced to kneel, with one hand holding the other behind me, and lick Snyder's fetid feet. By the way, you might be interested to know that sexy Joel and hunky Danny didn't spend all night tied to the staircase. The two of them were stripped buck-naked, and they were bound and gagged and stuffed into Snyder's car. They were driven around campus, one on top of the other with their feet sticking out of the window. Their tour ended when they were dumped out, still tied up and naked, to spend the evening on the front porch of a sorority house. Danny told me about it later, and he loved it, and I believe him, although Joel denied everything.

ACTIVES FUCK FROSH

🏛

When I was a lowly pledge, a fresh-scrubbed apple-cheeked 18-year-old, we got tied up all the time, and were often fucked or face fucked in the deal. Actives stripped us down, tied us up and flogged our cherry asses raw and rose red. This was throughout initiation and at other times that first year. Ropes, tapes, handcuffs and a dog collar were used on us. Unless we were told to suck a cock or three, we were almost always gagged, and I grew to groove on the thought of an active gagging me. The gags were usually rags or handkerchiefs stuffed in your mouth, with a piece of tape or another rag around the mouth. But sometimes our masters got creative and gagged us with pissed-on towels, dirty socks, day old jockeys and/or neckties.

Hell Week could have been renamed Naked Week, since pledges couldn't wear anything in the house and the actives weren't exactly overdressed either. They gave us T-shirts and shorts to wear to class, but we had to go barefoot. And though they provided the clothing, you had to grovel before your Big Brother for permission to put them on, or for anything else. They'd agree, but under certain conditions, meaning that you'd spend an afternoon performing their mindless errands, and spent the night tied up in the lounge or in their bed. Being naked, it was easy to be dragged into a room and abused, or forced to suck, get sucked or get fucked. And always bound and restrained.

In fact, I got my first fucking during Hell Week. I was tied down naked on a table, gagged, blindfolded, hands and feet spread wide, with two pillows under my groin that pushed up my ass. A fifth person fucked me as well, and from the muffled grunts he sounded like he was gagged and tied, too. So I don't know if this was an active who had to be forced into doing it with another guy, or maybe another active who just liked to be tied up, or maybe another pledge who was bound and forced to fuck to amuse the actives.

With all the forced sex, it was amazing that the upperclassmen would howl with anger if anyone hinted at being gay. They would laugh at somebody they thought was a "homo," then tie up a naked pledge and fuck him that night.

Another annual tradition was a coming out party, debutante-wise not sex identity-wise, to announce and show off the house pledges. We were paraded around North Campus bound and gagged and wearing our jockeys, led by an active playing bagpipes and another one beating a drum. No one within earshot could've ignored us, and guys in the other Houses and dorms came out to look us over. Other actives were there to make lots of noise, drink lots of beer and paddle our asses hard to keep the parade moving. A light steady rain was falling, and the underwear got soaked and our feet muddy. We gave a repeat performance for the sororities. One sorority joked that they wanted to buy us as slaves, but only if we remained tied and gagged.

After a year of this, revenge was best served cold. The last day of our freshman year, three of us soon to be upperclassmen dropped in on our Pledge Czar. That was his official title. He was a senior, and had to hang around until graduation the next weekend. Let's make this story short. We reminisced, got nostalgic, got him drunk, and got him hogtied with his own rope on his bed. It was his favorite way to tie us up. We gagged him with his socks, but not before he shouted for help. A neighbor knocked on the door to investigate.

We let him in and had him gagged before he could scream. This was another fair haired boy who'd dished out a lot of torture, so he had it coming. We rolled him on the floor and tied his hands behind his back. We got his shoes off his big feet and tied his feet to the bottom of the Czar's bed. In a flash of drama, I tore the T-shirt off his bare back and used the pieces to blindfold both of them. The three of us locked the door behind us, grabbed our luggage and beat a hasty retreat to the airport to catch planes home for summer. Of course they got themselves untied as we knew they would, but not before we were out of harm's way. But we heard that they thought it was a riot.

BILLIARD TABLE
BONDAGE

When I was a freshman a decade ago, I was too independent for Greek life, but I got roped into an initiation anyway. I worked in the game center of the student union, and before I could lock up for the night I had to toss out the rowdy frat boys in the billiards room. They'd signed out the room for a private party, and locked the doors. When I unlocked the door to break up the party, the place was a mess, but that's not what surprised me. Three hot looking pledges, their shirts off and pants unzipped, were tied and gagged on three pool tables, arms and legs stretched to the corners and roped down tight. The pledges were moaning and squirming in their places because the actives were dripping hot candle wax on their chests, navels and genitals.

The bound and tortured bodies on the tables belonged to Andy, Hutch and Pat. All three were freshmen in my Econ class. I said, very matter of fact, "Let's go guys, time to lock up." I thought I sounded very man of the world, like we were used to guys getting tied up on our pool tables all the time. But the actives took offense and glared at me, not like they'd been caught at something kinky, but as if to say, "Who are you to dare disturb us?"

"Grab him!" someone said, and actives were all over me. Hell, I don't think I'm a pushover at 6'2" and 190 pounds, but they had me pinned with my face to the floor and peeled down to my underwear before I could catch my breath. One kept his hand over my mouth. The actives tied me, binding my wrists, ankles and knees with rope, really tight. I bit the hand around my mouth, and somebody covered my mouth with duct tape. The fuckheads laughed at the muffled sounds I made when I tried to yell and untie myself.

The frat guys took a few steps back to admire their spread eagled boys, whose chests glistened with the hardening wax. They held a candle to the bottom of my bared feet, and then let several drops of hot wax dribble on my legs and cloth-covered crotch. The pain was real, but it wasn't as bad as my terrified mind had feared. But it was enough! I jerked and howled in pain and pleasure, which got a rise out of the frat boys.

We were left to our own bound devices for the night! Andy, Hutch and Pat gave out a collective gagged groan when they saw the actives depart. From the floor, all I could see were bound hands and feet on the side of the tables.

It took an hour of sweaty struggles, maybe more, but I finally got out of the ropes and slipped free. I thought about leaving the others spreadeagled on the tables. But they looked like they'd had enough for one night, and pleaded with their eyes like mistreated puppy dogs. I untied them slowly. They were sufficiently grateful, Hutch even hugged me, which transferred some of the wax on his chest to mine.

No real harm had been done, despite the mess, so I told them I wouldn't report the assault to the campus kops if they would help me clean the place up. Getting their frat in trouble wouldn't make their initiation any easier, I told them, so Hutch, Andy and Pat made like busy beaver housecleaners, and it was like having three personal slaves naked from the waist up and barefoot, ready to do my bidding. The actives had taken their shirts and shoes away when they left, so they were forced to walk back to the dorms with me stripped to their Levis and barefoot. But it was two in the morning on a Wednesday, so who noticed?

NON-FRATERNITY
INITIATIONS

CHASTENING
SUPERSTUD FARMBOY

Although the small, church-related college I attended in north west Missouri permitted no Greek letter organizations, with their traditional fondness for mistreating pledges, nevertheless our entire freshman class was subjected to a fairly lengthy period of initiation which, at times, spilled over unabashedly into the realm of hazing. Freshman initiation culminated on what was known as "Scrap Day," the principal activity of which was a tug-of-war between the freshmen and sophomore boys over an enormous water-filled mud pit which had been dug by the freshmen boys during the midnight hours of the previous weeks. If the freshmen won, all hazing came to an immediate end on that Friday afternoon. In the event the sophomores won, the initiation period was extended until the Thanksgiving holidays.

While the boys were digging the pit each night, the girls of the freshman class were made to serenade them. Boys waiting to take another turn at digging were kept busy doing calisthenics. Vigorous participation was encouraged by upperclassmen wielding heavy wooden paddles which were passed down from year to year.

On one such night during my senior year, I observed a cocky freshman boy being paddled for not doing pushups to the satisfaction of the sophomore standing over him. Later, back in the dorm, I overheard this kid in the shower gleefully telling his roommate how he had outsmarted the system by padding the rear pockets of his Levis. It seems that he had put his wallet in one pocket and his cigarette case in the other. These things, plus the natural padding provided by his jeans and underwear had rendered the paddling virtually painless.

My irritation upon overhearing this conversation was compounded by what I had observed of this guy during the previous four or five weeks. Here was a hunky little 5'7" Iowa farmboy, who obviously pictured himself as "Superstud," strutting around the campus acting like God's gift to the world. I was also massively pissed by the arrogant "fuck you" attitude he displayed toward all upperclassmen.

Having discussed this situation with three close friends, we decided it was time to teach Mr. Superstud farmboy a lesson in humility. During the next two days we carefully made our preparations in the barn of an abandoned farm three miles out in the country, accessible only by a little used and badly rutted dirt road. On the chosen night, we ambushed David as he was leaving the library at closing time. Having attacked him from behind on the darkest part of the path, we managed to have him blindfolded and gagged before he had a chance to recognize us. Since we were not in his class, there was little chance of his identifying us by our voices. After taping his eyes shut with duct tape, which we wrapped all around his head, we stuffed a thick sock into his mouth. The sock was kept firmly in place by again wrapping tape around his entire head. With his eyes and mouth secured, we covered David's head using as a hood a small stuffy bag, the drawstrings of which were tightly tied around his neck. After wrestling David belly-down into the grass, two of us fastened his ankles together while the other two tied his hands behind his back. Within seconds, David found himself hogtied, wrapped in a canvas tarp, bouncing down a bumpy country road in the bed of a pickup truck.

Upon arrival at our destination, we allowed David to remain hogtied on the floor of the barn while we lit the lanterns we had hung on posts. After untying the ropes connecting his hands and feet, we pulled David into a standing position. Since our plan was that David be stripped completely naked for his punishment, it was obviously necessary to untie his wrists and remove the headbag in order to facilitate the removal of his T-shirt. This being accomplished, David's head was once again bagged and his wrists retied in front to a length of rope which had been tossed over an overhead beam.

As soon as David had been suspended so that only his toes were touching the ground, I began to deliver my carefully prepared lecture. I told him that the best-known, time-honored cure for a cocky attitude in a pain-in-the-ass Iowa farmboy was a trip to the woodshed. However it had been decided that, since he had not been able to learn his lesson with his pants on, it would be necessary to try it another way.

Realizing that he was in for a bad time, David began to wriggle as best he could as we popped the buttons on his 501s. After untying his ankles, David's cowboy boots and socks were removed and were quickly followed by his jeans.

At this point, David had stopped struggling and was quietly hanging there, apparently resigned to his fate. I gently slipped my fingers inside the waistband of David's jockeys, reminding him that these would have to come off so that he would be better able to feel the whipping he would be getting in a few minutes. I also told him that, before his whipping began, he had yet another lesson in humility in store for him. Perhaps he would feel less like Mr. Cocky Superstud if he was forced to be seen in gym class and in the showers minus his thick pelt of body fur. By the time the four of us were finished with the lathering and shaving, David's body fairly gleamed in the lantern light with not a hair to be seen anywhere, even on his armpits or gonads.

Before letting David down from his suspended position, we tied a length of rope to the base of his penis, coiling it around the top of his scrotal sac, tying the loose end to the loop in the top of one of his cowboy boots. As we dropped the boot into thin air, we heard a quick hiss of air escape from David's nostrils as his body lurched involuntarily.

While releasing David from the overhead beam, we informed him that the time had now come for his whipping. I had just recently read some naval history to the effect that whereas full-grown men used to be tied upright to gratings on board ship to have their backs flogged, boys serving as midshipmen would be positioned over a cannon, buttocks up, for a caning. After telling David this story, we informed him that, since he had not yet learned to behave as a mature adult male, he would have to be punished in the style of a snotnosed, immature boy, which was all the more appropriate anyway, considering the fact that he was totally lacking in body hair. We then laid him over an old waist-high saw horse, which we had previously padded with burlap sacks, and tied his wrists and ankles securely to the legs.

With his upraised bare buttocks making a perfect target, and with the boot swinging gently between his legs, the four of us slid our belts out of our pants and took turns leathering David's tight little ass. As the sound of the belts cracked in the cool night air, the four of us unloaded all the verbal abuse which had been building up inside us. Gordon asked David how it felt to be getting it without the benefit of clothing and padding? Doyle added his hope that the lessons we were trying to teach would help David grow into a more likable human being, which he certainly was not at the moment. As Rich took his crack at the now bright red ass, he suggested that, the next time David was spotted around the pit with anything at all in his back pockets, he should have his pants taken down on the spot and turned over to the girls for paddling. By the time we were finished, David's ass was a shambles and his sobbing was clearly audible even through the gag and hood.

After loading our lanterns and gear into Rich's pickup, we untied David and led him naked and barefoot, with the boot still hanging from his balls, out into the middle of the deserted country road. We told him that, as soon as he heard the engine crank up, he could remove his blindfold and gag and head back into town. We left him his socks, boots, T-shirt and briefs. His Levis he would find later back at the dorm, neatly folded and lying just outside his door. Inside the right front pocket he would also discover a note of warning which read: "Remember, there's more where this came from."

Just before leaving David standing there still blindfolded and shivering, I suggested to him that he use the walk back to town as a time to contemplate ways in which his behavior might be different in the future. As I finished my lecture, I noticed that Doyle had pulled something out of his pocket and was fastening it around David's neck. It was a choker-length piece of steel link chain which Doyle proceeded to lock on with a small but very strong padlock. Doyle whispered in David's ear that he would be required to wear his new slave collar as a reminder of the lessons he was being taught. Assuming David would prove himself an able learner, the key to the padlock would appear under his door just before he left for the Thanksgiving holidays.

A more chastened, reformed David would be difficult to

imagine. I will confess to feeling some slight remorse when I noticed that, in removing the tape, some of the hairs of his very neat crew cut had been pulled out, leaving him with a somewhat molted look. But I wasn't at all sorry to notice the stiffness of David's walk for the next few days, or the way in which he sat down, slowly and very gingerly. But, best of all was his transformation in attitude. When quizzed about either his bright red ass or the chain around his neck, David's stock answer would be something to the effect of, "I have some upperclassmen friends who are helping me to become a better person."

When, two days later, I decided to test the waters for myself by ordering him to "button," David couldn't get down on his knees fast enough to recite the stupid jingle which was required memory work for all freshmen:

> I'm a stupid little freshman
> just as green as I can be.
> I'll honor upperclassmen
> wherever they may be.

And, do you know what? I really believe he actually meant it!

JOINING
THE HOUSE

🏛

I had transferred from a college back east to a college in California. When I got to town a couple of days before school started, I needed to find somewhere to live fast. Checking the papers I noticed one that really seemed to be made for me. It said:

> *Wanted: roommate to share very large house with 15 other guys. Must be good at basketball, softball, flag football and other intramural sports.*

When I knocked on the door, it was opened by a very large, extremely ripped and muscular guy, about 6'0", 170 lbs., wearing tight jeans and a string tank top, showing off a good part of his massive, thick, muscular chest. He had cleavage you could get lost in and one of his big brown nipples was poking out of his top. He was obviously a bodybuilder.

Since I lift weights I figured we had something in common. I told him I was there about the ad. He introduced himself as Randy and invited me in.

He told me about the situation. He said that the house was more like a club. They had won or placed in the top four in intramural and city flag football, basketball, softball, weightlifting and, even water polo, along with some other sports. He said that they were more than roommates, they were like brothers, which is why, he felt, they played so well together.

I asked him if they were all about his size. If they were, I figured that might be why they won so much.

We talked for several more minutes, when another guy came in. He was introduced as Scott. He was about an inch or two taller than Randy, and even though he was very muscular, he didn't have nearly the build of Randy. However, when we shook hands I realized that he had a grip.

Scott had dark hair and eyes and if he hadn't been standing beside Randy would be considered very good looking with a very good build.

They asked me questions about my athletic prowess. I had played High School football, basketball, baseball, and powerlifted, and had lettered in all of them. I played football last year at my other college, but had gotten hurt. Even though I probably shouldn't play regular football, I could play flag football and other sports with no problem.

At that point, several other incredible looking guys came in and each asked me several questions. I had been through job interviews that had been easier. But it was worth it. I was impressed with the guys and was very impressed with the rent.

The house wasn't bad either. It was a big old house in very good shape. I could see a big screen tv from the living room that was on ESPN. It looked like a pool table was there too.

After a few minutes they asked me if I could wait in the hall while they had a meeting. Now I really felt like it was a job interview. After a while Randy, Scott and a couple of the guys came out and asked me if I would be interested in rooming with them. They all shook my hand, patted me on the back and butt.

Randy seemed to be the leader of the group. He told me that since sports were very important to them there would be a month's probationary period, during which they would see if I would fit in. I had nowhere else to go so I said yes.

I moved in right away. A couple nights later I attended my first club meeting in the living room. A couple of those guys were married. Four were alumni, who didn't play intramural sports but did play on the city leagues. I was told that there were other alumni who did the same. I would meet them as they often came over.

All the guys were big. Chris, a wrestler, was the shortest at about 5'10" and Scott the tallest at about 6'5". All of them were very muscular. I also learned that most of them were practical jokers, especially Randy, the best built of the group. He and Jeff, another bodybuilder, would often team up in doing pranks against the others. I was told that I would be fairly safe for a day or two or until I started pulling pranks on them, whichever came first.

Every Saturday night was competition night. It was just an in-house competition where anything that could be turned into a competition would be. And I was told that I would be expected to show up since I was on probation. The first week was a competition in pool. I came in seventh of fourteen.

After the competition, I went out. When I got back, I was going to go straight upstairs to bed, but I heard a moaning sound in the rec room. I went in.

I turned on the lights and saw Chris tied spread-eagled to the pool table. Each thick wrestler's arm and leg was tied to the corner pockets. He was shirtless, and I noticed how hairy his thick chest was. He had clips attached to his nipples and the club name painted on his chest with magic marker. He was almost wearing a pair of jeans. They had been pulled down as far as possible with his legs being spread-eagle as they were. He was gagged with several layers of athletic tape.

He had a big hard on with good sized nuts and I was getting excited seeing him flex and stretch against the ropes. He was trying to yell through the tape but all I could understand was "MMMMMM."

I started laughing, but he moaned and looked at me with his big, sad brown eyes. I wasn't sure if I should let him go or not. I didn't want to get in trouble with the other guys. However, I didn't want to get into trouble with him either. I explained my situation to him and told him that I really wanted to live here and be part of the house with the other guys. I asked him if my chances would be hurt if I let him go. He moaned and shook his head no.

I cut him loose and he got up and hugged me, even before he took the gag out or zipped his pants. He took the gag out and said, "Thanks, man. I've been there for a couple of hours. No one was really supposed to let me go until morning, but I won't tell if you won't. I'll just say that I got myself loose."

He went to zip up his pants and I noticed that he had a red ribbon tied around the base of his dick. I asked him about it and he said that it was what the loser had to wear all week.

I asked him if being tied to the table was part of losing, also. He said not exactly. Since he was the one to lose at pool, he was the obvious choice as victim of a prank. He did tell me that if anyone found out that I had let him go, I would be there next as a replacement. He said that we had better go to bed before we were caught. He said that he would go up first so no one would suspect me of letting him go. I was to wait a few minutes, then go up.

The second week's contest was pushups and situps. I came

in about tenth. I ran to the library to get a book. When I got back, a group of the guys were in the living room. Scott was lying on the floor, stark naked.

His feet were tied together, as were his knees. His hands were tied behind his head with the rope going under his arms. He had several layers of athletic tape over his mouth, to gag him. He had the club name painted on his chest like Chris had the week before.

He had a big hard on and some of the biggest balls I had ever seen. Scott is practically hairless, except for a thick, almost black patch of dark fur around his dick and the same stuff under his arms. He had a red ribbon tied around his dick like Chris did last week. They were making him do situps in that position.

A couple of the guys would give his big, brown nipples a workout if he stayed on the floor too long, or they would give his very hairy dick and balls flicks with their fingers. Both seemed to inspire him to continue.

After I had been there for several minutes, a couple of the guys noticed me and told me that I had better leave since I wasn't officially in the house yet. I stayed a minute longer and Gary, who looked as hot as Randy kind of shouted that I would be there with Scott in a minute if I didn't take off. I almost decided to stay.

A few days later, intramural football started, we would practice about twice a week, and surprisingly again, about the whole house would show up. I was impressed that I was doing as well as I was and it was a lot of fun. The guys in the house were great guys. I was hoping that I would pass the probationary period.

We won our first game. I only played about two minutes, but

felt like I did pretty well. The game wasn't even close. The only mistake our team made was by Kevin, who had missed the field goal.

It didn't bother me because everyone makes mistakes every once in a while and besides, I really liked Kevin. He was muscular like the other guys, but maybe not quite as toned. He had brownish red hair and brown eyes, but his beard and pubes were pretty red and he got a bit of hazing for that, but took it and dished out more. He was always ready to pull a prank and laughed easily. He also had the longest dong I had ever seen.

Anyway, after the game, several of the guys jumped Kevin, stripped him to his jock and taped him up with athletic tape. They worked like a well oiled machine, each man having his responsibility and looking like they had done this before.

They taped his ankles together, his knees, his hands behind him and then wrapped several lengths around him just for good measure. Then they hung him upside down from the goal post. He was also gagged. I must admit that he looked pretty funny hanging there in only his jock. They painted the team name on his chest and each guy signed his name to Kevin's naked butt. I guessed that this was his punishment for missing the field goal.

They finished, took some pictures and we all left, with Kevin moaning in the background. I was kind of worried about leaving him there by himself and said something to Randy about it. I was told very curtly that since I wasn't in the club, it was none of my business unless I wanted to be there with him.

That week the competitions were the quarter test (holding a quarter in the cleavage of your chest for the longest) and a drinking test (each drank about a gallon of water to see who went to the bathroom first).

I did okay. Randy and Jeff and a couple of the other guys used dollar bills instead of quarters and still kept it there the longest.

I did okay in the drinking test, too, until we had to put ice in our underwear.

I had a late date that night, but I couldn't help wondering what punishment would be inflicted on Pat, who lost the quarter test, and Mike, who lost the drinking test. When I got home, very late that night, nothing strange seemed to have happened, but I stayed awake fantasizing about what I would do to the losers. I even walked around to see if I could find anyone tied up.

A couple days later, we won our second game. I got to play about half the game and made an interception and scored a touchdown. I felt pretty good. I was told that I would be told that Sunday if I could stay and be part of the club. I felt like I would be in until some of the guys told me that even though I played pretty well, my scores in the weekly competitions hadn't been all that great. I was determined to do better on Saturday.

When I went to the competition on Saturday, I was told that it was a tying contest. Each person's number was put in a hat. The first six drawn were the tied, the second six were the tie-ers.

The top had five minutes to tie up his victim. Then each person was timed to see how long it took him to get loose. The bottom got points by being fast. The top lost points if his victim was fast. Then it was switched. The tied became the tie-ers. It usually took several rounds to place the winner, so I had better plan to stay all night and even into tomorrow.

There were also other rules: We started off shirtless and in gym shorts. After the man was tied, ten minutes later he would be blindfolded; after another ten minutes he would be gagged;

after ten more minutes a piece of clothes would be removed; after each ten minute block more clothes could be removed, after that another length of rope could be added.

By the luck of the draw, I was to be a top on the first round. My victim was to be Eric. A big guy with dark red hair, and lots of freckles. He seemed like the strong silent type when I first met him, but he had since pulled a lot of pranks on me. He was also one of my staunchest supporters to be in the club and one of my favorite people in the house.

I felt guilty tying him, and kept apologizing, but needed to do a good job so I could stay in the club and in the house. I had Eric sit in a chair like all the others. I had him put his arms over the back of the chair with them hanging down. Then I tied his wrists. I tied an extra length of rope to a bar that went across the bottom of the chair. I was careful to make sure that the knots were away from anywhere he could reach. I then tied his ankles and knees to the legs of the chair. Then I took a few lengths of rope around his chest and arms.

When the five minute whistle sounded, I felt like I had done a good job. Sure enough after ten minutes, I blindfolded him, but no one else was loose either. After ten minutes more I gagged him. He fought it and told me what he would do to me when it was his turn. I finally gave him a hard little twist on his big pink tits and as he gasped, I rammed the gag into his mouth and tied it shut. His ruddy complexion turned red. I hoped that I hadn't lost a friend and supporter. Konrad got loose right before the third ten minute buzzer sounded. At least my victim wasn't the first, I thought.

At the third ten minute buzzer, I ripped Eric's shorts off. I couldn't just pull them off because of the way he was tied. I could tell that made him even madder, but he was still tied. I realized that when he tied me, I was in trouble. He was sitting there in a jock, with a blindfold and gag on. Pretty much unable to move. He looked incredibly hot. I had never seen his bare legs and butt before.

They were very muscular and his legs had a thin coat of bright red hair. His butt was incredible, too. Two pink, hard melons crammed together. I was getting excited and so were many of the guys. Three of them got undone. There were only Eric and Kevin who were still tied. This should get me some points.

When the fourth buzzer rang, I ripped off his jock, exposing his red pubes and long, thick dick. Now he started really struggling hard. I could almost understand the swearing through the gag.

At the fifth buzzer I used the rope to tie his wrists again. I patted him on the head and apologized again. I could tell that he felt like he was defeated. About that time, Kevin got undone. Chris, his tie-er, didn't realize that as he tied his upper arms Kevin got out of his wrist rope. I had won this round.

I went to start to untie Eric and Randy told me not to. One of the other guys would get me until he got loose. I didn't want to leave him there, but I did. I needed to stay in the house. I guessed Eric would have to keep struggling for a while. I could tell he was shouting at me through the gag. Randy took a red ribbon and tied it around the base of Eric's dick and balls. It seemed like Eric hung his head in defeat.

I sat down in the chair with nothing on but shorts and socks. Pat drew to tie me. Somebody said I was lucky because Pat didn't know how to tie a knot. I was nervous. I had to get undone fast to make sure I was in the club. Everyone (except Eric) told me that I had done a great job in tying Eric. I glanced over at him while I was being tied.

Pat wrapped the rope around my wrists a few times. I tried to flex so when I relaxed the rope would be loose. He wrapped the rope around my ankles and knees, finishing me off with a few loops around my chest and upper arms.

At the five minute buzzer I was still struggling. However, at ten minutes I still hadn't gotten far. Again I glanced over at Eric struggling, while Pat put a blindfold on me. I did feel like I was starting to make progress when the second buzzer sounded.

Even though Pat didn't know how to tie knots, he knew how to gag. At least from the sound of the group, no one else was undone either. When the third buzzer sounded, I was almost undone, but I still lost my shorts. When I ripped the blindfold off, everyone else was still tied.

I glanced over and saw that Eric was just getting loose. I went over and asked if he was okay and apologized again. He gave me a manly hug and patted my butt. He laughed and said that it was all part of the game and that someday he would get even. Since he had lost all his clothes in the competition he had to walk around naked the rest of the evening. You could tell that he was a little embarrassed about it. His red face clashed with his hair.

There were half a dozen guys in the same predicament and it was great! All of them were terrific looking and well hung. Many had hard ons which a lot of the still dressed guys laughed at and pointed at.

Matt, a big muscular blond with a seemingly mean face, but a real practical joker of a personality said that he thought the next contest should be "Longest Dong." He was known to be very well endowed and I agreed with him.

It was about twenty more minutes before the next to last guy got loose. Again they left the last guy, Dave, to fend for himself and tied a red ribbon around his nuts.

There was another round of tying that I wasn't involved in. So I had some beers and cheered the guys on. Several guys came over and asked if I wanted to be a brother in the house. I said, "Definitely," and "Sure." Then they would pat me on the back and smile and hand me a beer. In a short while, I could feel a buzz. I decided that I couldn't drink anymore. I didn't want to get drunk during this. I felt like my chances were pretty good at getting in the club and I didn't want to blow it.

After a couple rounds (probably a couple hours or more) Randy announced that so far there was a tie. Konrad and I. There was to be a tie-breaker. The same guy would tie us both up, identically, this time taking ten minutes on each of us. The rest of the group met to decide who it would be.

A couple minutes later, I saw a big smile cross Eric's face and I knew I was in trouble. We both sat in the chairs, Konrad still had shorts on while I was just in a jock. He hadn't lost his in the last round while I had. Eric decided to get Konrad first.

Konrad was probably the strongest guy in the club, including Randy, Jeff and Gary, the bodybuilders. He had sandy hair, thick chest and arms, big muscular butt and legs. He had a sprinkling of hair on his huge chest with a circle around his big nipples. He was another one who seemed mean and serious until you got to know him. Then he was a big-time practical joker.

Eric tied Konrad much like I had tied Eric, except he didn't tie his feet or ankles, but used more rope on his wrists, upper arms, around his chest, waist, etc. That made me feel like there was hope.

He got me next. I realized right away that I was in trouble, even with my legs free. When Eric finished he gave me a quick nuggie and a tittie twist and winked his eye. Right then the buzzer sounded to start. At ten minutes I hadn't gotten anywhere.

Randy went over to blindfold Konrad, while Eric came over to me, leaned over and started to pull my jock off. I yelled in protest and said that clothes came off after the third buzzer. The first buzzer was a blindfold. Eric laughed and said that he was going to blindfold me with my jock so it was okay. He then put the band over my eyes and secured it with athletic tape. The cup hung over my nose and straps were put behind my ears.

Eric was getting back at me all right. I didn't have anything on but socks and didn't feel like I was getting anywhere with the ropes. I struggled harder. The second buzzer sounded. It didn't sound like Konrad was free yet. Someone (I soon found out it was Eric) started to take off my socks. Since my legs were free I started kicking and said again that clothes couldn't be removed until the third buzzer, that this was... I stopped. I suddenly realized that he was going to gag me with my own socks. I was right. Eric started to gag me. I fought but he was rough. He gagged me good.

So much time had passed while I was trying to keep from getting gagged the third buzzer sounded almost immediately. Eric said that since I wasn't wearing anything to take off, the rules said that they could go right into the next step of adding another piece of rope. Randy said that he was right. I didn't think Konrad was loose yet, but I knew I was in trouble.

Much to my surprise, Eric took the rope and tied it around

my balls, then around my wrists, then back around my balls and the base of my dick. Every time I tried to do anything with my wrists, I pulled on my balls. Eric gave me a tittie twist, rubbed my head and said that he told me he would get even. My dick started to swell even more than it already had. Everyone was laughing at it.

The buzzer went off again. This time I heard a shout from Konrad that he was free. It occurred to me that there was no way he could get free if he was getting the same treatment I was. Eric told me that when the man got free, the rope that was used on him could be used on the person still tied. Randy agreed. I moaned through the gag.

Very quickly my legs were tied and a length of rope was taken several times around my chest and arms. I knew I would never get out. I decided that the guys had decided that they didn't want me and this was the punishment. I figured that they would take me to the girls' dorm like this or to the mall, or maybe they'd drop me off in the woods.

Then the rope was tied around the head of my dick and wound around the back of my neck and tied to the head of my dick again. Rope was then tied again to my feet, around to my wrists, to my balls, and then back to my feet.

I literally couldn't move, make a sound or see anything. The guys started yanking on the ropes around my dick and balls, giving me tittie twisters, rubbing my head and telling me good night. Eric, Randy and Konrad were the last. They said that the party would continue later, that they had to make some preparations. My balls and dick were aching.

The buzzer kept sounding every ten minutes, I imagined. I kept losing track of how many times it went off. It seemed like about a half dozen, when I felt someone playing with my nipples. I moaned in surprise. No one said anything. I got worried that it wasn't one of the guys. I wasn't in a very defendable position. Whoever it was walked around me and tugged on the ropes, checking them to make sure they were tight. A couple of times whoever it was tightened the ropes.

He squeezed my cheeks to check the gag and checked the blindfold. I then heard him go into the kitchen. A couple minutes later he was back and started rubbing ice all over me. I was going crazy, but I couldn't struggle much, because of my balls being tied. He then crammed some ice into my butt and under my balls and left.

I was left again for quite a while after that. The buzzer went off several more times. Someone else came and started doing something to my nipples again. It felt like he was drawing on them. He then started on the top of my dick. I still couldn't move and it tickled. He stopped and I was left again. The buzzer sounded several more times.

All of a sudden, my chair and I were lifted up. It's happening, I thought, they are going to put me outside or at the girls' dorm or something. But it felt like I was going downstairs. My chair was put down and I felt someone's hands on my shoulders. I heard Eric's voice whisper to me, "Don't worry, you're okay, you're not going to get hurt, this is the beginning of your initiation into the Club."

I heard Randy's voice next. He told me that if I wanted to be a member I should nod once. He said that if I didn't they would take me back upstairs, let me go and there would be no hard feelings on their part. Before I could nod, he told me that the vote had been unanimous and that Eric would be my big brother if I wanted to go through with it. He said that this was the beginning of a ten-week process, but that the rewards would be to have a great group of brothers and to be a member of a team of great athletes. I nodded yes. Eric rubbed my head and gave my nipple a friendly twist. "Good," he said. Randy gave my balls a painful squeeze and announced, "Let it begin."

THE NEW
TEAM CAPTAIN

🏛

I was 19, and a sophomore in school. It was the end of my team's spring season, and I had just been elected captain for next year (in something of an upset). Normally, the team didn't haze its players very hard; initiations consisted of drinking a bit of beer, being thrown in the shower, or being "flesh-piled" or "gang-tackled." However, as an uppity sophomore (and a captain!), I received some special treatment.

On the fateful night, I was lying peacefully asleep in my dorm room when the door burst open and three of my teammates leapt on me, rope in hand. The struggle was brief and one-sided, and I quickly found my wrists tied tightly behind me with my arms crossed, and with rope bound tightly around my bare ankles and above my knees. At some point I yelled for help to my roommate (who appeared to be sleeping through all this, although he later admitted to me that he just didn't want to get involved). This brought one of my captors' hands across my mouth. "Better gag him," someone said. I felt a sock being stuffed in my mouth, and another sock was tied around my head, painfully tight, to keep it in place. I was blindfolded with one of my own bandannas. I was sleeping naked, as usual, so they rolled me up in one of my blankets and dragged me out to a car (*my* car, in fact). I was thrown into the back seat, and off we went.

During the ride I tried struggling with my bonds, and particularly with the wretched gag, but to no avail. I did manage to scrape my blindfold off, but it was immediately tied back on (much tighter, of course). My companions tried to cheer me up by hinting at all the dire things in store for me as the car twisted and turned through the narrow streets of campus. When we stopped, they carried me into a building and down some steps. They laid me down on a rug, which smelled of stale beer. The rope around my ankles was fastened to a post, so that my legs and ass were lifted off the ground and I was lying on my back and shoulders. "Don't go away," they said. I didn't.

It seemed like I lay there for a long time, but it was probably only a few minutes before I heard people coming back. The rope holding my ankles up was released, and quickly fastened to something else. Rather, I should say some*one* else, since I was being tied face-to-face with another bound person. We were bound together with rope at our ankles, at our waists, and under and around our arms. I couldn't tell who the other person was, except that he was shorter than I was and had shorts on. He was clearly gagged and blindfolded as well. At this point we were told that this was a test of our ability to work together as captain and co-captain, and that we had fifteen minutes to free ourselves or we would each get twenty whacks with the paddle. The paddle was demonstrated once on each of us, as incentive, I suppose. At least I knew who my involuntary buddy was; it was my co-captain, Dave. Well, we provided fifteen minutes of entertainment for our audience (most of the team), and we managed to rub our blindfolds and our gags off of each other's faces, but there was no chance of untying the knots. We rolled around a lot and worked up a good sweat, but that was about it. Once time was called, our captors jumped on us and competed to see who could swat our asses the hardest with the ping-pong paddles. We each got thirty strokes (they were getting pretty drunk, and could hardly count).

At this point I started getting a hard-on while lying beneath Dave. I could feel every muscle in his body twitch when he was hit. It was an amazing sensation—I don't think I've ever felt closer to anyone in my life. For what it's worth, Dave had a hard-on too, and he was as straight as they come. After it was all over, I thought about talking to him about it, but I never had the nerve. I tried setting up a similar initiation for our successors, but it never worked out.

GYMNAST INITIATION

My fraternity initiation was just a lot of drunken humiliation. But my college gymnastics team had an initiation ritual that made up for my fraternity's deficiency. After tryouts the gymnastics team always did a three day training retreat at a lodge near campus to do workouts, weight training, bonding and all that nonsense. It was common knowledge that the newest team members, namely a guy named Elon and myself that year, got put through the wringer in some sort of initiation. How true. Before we could get into the van for the trip, Elon and I had our shirts pulled off much against our will. Our hands were tied and we were gagged and blindfolded. The seat belt was a turn on across my bare chest. The coach went along with this, talking about this being good clean fun.

The fun really began once we arrived. For every lap the team ran or every pushup or whatever, Elon and I did two or three. On top of that, the two of us worked out naked and barefoot while the rest of the team kept their shorts and shoes on. This included a naked jog in the great outdoors over gravel roads and sharp stones, with our hands tied behind us.

After working out on the rings, we both spent several aching minutes with our wrists tied to the rings, twisting slowly in the hot lodge gym with a concrete block tied to our bound feet hanging a few inches off the floor. The guys called it a strength stretch, I called it a great excuse to get a naked boy in bondage.

While Elon was stretched from the rings, I was tied to the parallel bars gagged with a rope in my mouth, and vice versa. We also had to do power situps with our feet bound and our hands tied behind our heads. The rope was tied tight around the shoulder and under my arms, which kept me from trying to move my hands from their restrictive position.

They let us shower and dress around suppertime, but we didn't stay dressed long. Later that night when Coach wasn't around, a couple of the guys escorted me to the cellar of the conference center for what sounded like an innocent bullshit session. When I got there, I was tackled and stripped to my BVDs. My hands were bound and a piece of rope wrapped between my teeth a couple of times and around my head. Poor Elon was already stripped down and gagged and tied to a post, struggling to free his hands bound over his head. They tied me to the other side of the post, arms pulled way over my head. And we were thrown at, spit at, manhandled and beaten with branches and a small whip. We were even just plain tickled. Neither Elon nor I were beaten bloody or anything, but we had red stripes in unusual places for days. They led us upstairs when they finished with us, and tied us face up on our beds for the night.

The second day was a rerun of the first. More naked workouts and jogging, hands bound when they weren't needed. I'm amazed at how much abuse we were willing to put up with without complaints. Elon and I talked about that in a rare ungagged moment alone. We really wanted to belong, and we made a silent pact to take whatever the team dished out to prove ourselves.

In the afternoon, while Coach looked on, Elon and I gave a

forced impromptu wrestling match, stark naked. The loser had to do extra laps and situps. I won and got out of doing extra exercises, but Coach didn't know that my so called rest period was spent bound and gagged on my bed.

The grand finale took place during a late swim at a nearby pond. A few beers into the twilight, we were grabbed and gagged with rope again. This was a planned attack. The guys brought along a couple of sturdy two-by-fours, about six feet long and hidden from us until the magic moment. Our trunks came off, and we were each tied to a board, with our wrists and ankles tied around the board in front of us. Each board was picked up and balanced on the shoulders of two guys, one in front and one behind. Between them, our bodies dangling underneath the two-by-fours, held by our roped feet and hands, we looked like prize calves bound for slaughter.

The team made a lot of ceremony and noise about carrying Elon and me to our doom. We got slaps and an occasional kick as we were carried from the pond back to that torturous cellar. There, we were tightly bound face up on a table side by side, hands roped together and pulled over our heads and feet tied together as well. The ropes were tied to the underside of the table and movement was nearly impossible and unthinkable. Elon was making incoherent groaning noises regardless of the rope gag, and I joined him as he screamed for release.

We were blindfolded with towels or some other white cloths. The team captain told us that we had to shake with the team before we could become a full part of the varsity squad, and he didn't mean shake hands. I nearly jumped off the table, ropes or no ropes, when a hand grabbed my half hard dick and gave it a hard squeeze. Elon howled, too. His dick had also found a new friend. One after another, each guy on the team stroked my cock and pumped it, squeezing those tender balls in the process. They also plucked out some pubic hairs as they methodically jacked me off. Someone started yanking on the hairs of my armpits. I couldn't prepare myself for the pain and it really started to sting like crazy. I felt something rubbing against my toe and I tried to flick it away, but it wasn't a mosquito. A hand came down on my ankles, and I felt the rubbing sensation again. One comedian was painting our toenails.

I heard a groan to my left, followed by loud cheers from the team. Elon had cum, and from the carrying on you'd think the guys had struck oil. They stopped yanking my hairs and started giving me a serious hand job. Just as someone shouted that I didn't have any cum in me, I came and came gratefully before my appreciative unseen audience.

"Just one more night all tied up, boys," the team captain said. Still blindfolded, gagged and nude, we were untied and carefully led down the halls to our room. Elon and I had had the fight knocked out of us, so we gave in to their commands and lay down on our beds face down with arms and legs extended. Stretched to the four corners, we were roped down tight and got a barehanded spanking instead of a bedtime story.

Some time in the night, Elon worked out of his bonds. Instead of untying me, he started rubbing me and talking about how horny he was and about being naked and "fucking tortured" and that he was so horny he could "fuck a tree." There were no trees in the room, so I was elected. Elon said he'd untie me if I let myself get fucked up the ass. He said it over and over and started rhapsodising on the qualities of my ass as he climbed on top and fucked me.

Actually, I wasn't crazy about being fucked against my will at first. After all, Elon was a rookie on the team, too, so what did that make me? Oh, well. He did untie me, eventually.

By the way, we woke up early and managed to use our ropes to get another team member tied and gagged! He was one surprised Texan, and we earned brownie points for our ingenuity. We had to ride back to campus as we'd ridden to the lodge, bound and gagged and without our shirts, but it didn't matter. We felt like two of the guys, and the two of us knew we had a lot to talk about when we were alone. Elon was straight, or so he thought, and now he had a girlfriend and a boyfriend.

FIREMAN
INITIATION

🏛

Around eight years ago, when I was living in South Carolina, I joined the Bucket Brigade of my little town. The town was small and so they had a volunteer fire department made up of most of the able-bodied and a few not so able-bodied men in the town. The able-bodied ones interested me, but I was young and just out of the Army, and the military taught me how to keep my desires a secret.

Anyway, a couple of months after I joined the fire department, we had our annual barbeque at the fire house. It was one of the big events of the year, which should tell you how small the town is. By 9:00 or so, most of the kids and families had gone home and the only ones left were we brave firemen and a few friends, mostly male and getting sloshed. The fire captain said that the two rookie firemen, meaning me and my buddy Chase, had to be initiated. We knew that some sort of stupid ceremony would take place, but I didn't know what to think when the guys grabbed us and started tearing our clothes off!

They stripped us down to our socks and underwear, then they dragged us over to a chain-link fence in the backyard of the firehouse. Ever try to fight a drunken mob when you're half naked? It ain't easy. Their hands were all over us, and someone put their hand over my mouth till I promised to stop yelling.

To make a long story short, they tied us spread-eagle with our backs to the fence, with ropes tied around our outstretched wrists and feet. Naturally, I was trying not to show how much I was enjoying this, but ol' Chase was pissed and swearing loud enough to rouse the dead. One of the other firemen gagged him with a rag to shut him up, and gagged me, too!

For the rest of the night, we had to put up with their insults and name calling while the party continued. All night long, Chase and I were tied to that damn fence. We were splashed with beer, pop, whiskey, even barbecue sauce. One fucker grabbed my underwear and poured a bottle of beer down my crotch! Now I had see-through underwear. He left the beer bottle hanging upside-down in my underwear and spritzed me with the contents of another bottle.

Now that we were a pair of sticky sons of bitches, attracting every insect within miles to bite us, the Captain declared that Chase and I were full-fledged volunteer fitremen. But first we had to be baptized. Those fuckers turned on a fire hose and sprayed us good! It was sort of low pressure, thank God, but it was hard enough to sting and pin us against the fence if the ropes hadn't been there already, and we sure couldn't get out of the way.

Really soaked to the skin, Chase and I were untied and given towels and a couple of beers, and we joined in what was left of the party. But we didn't get our clothes back till the end of the night, meaning we had to be party animals in our skivvies. That was another part of the initiation. For some weird reason, I wasn't embarrassed being nude in front of those guys when I was tied up to that fence, but when I was untied and still naked I blushed red all night.

In the five years I lived there, each of the rookie volunteers, all four of them, went through pretty much the same initiation, stripped and tied to the chain-link fence. Twin Peaks had nothing on that crazy town.

I moved away but Chase is still down there and he wrote to tell me that it happened again just last month.

PUBLISHER'S AFTERWORD

All the accounts of school, frat, team and club initiations in this book originally appeared in the reader-written male bondage magazine, *Bound & Gagged*, and in two of its special publications, *Pledges & Paddles Volume 1* and *Volume 2*. Because of the nature of *Bound & Gagged*, there is an emphasis on the bondage aspect of hazing which, I am aware, is not so often present as would seem to be the case here. Nevertheless, the fact is that a lot of guys do get tied up in frat house and initiation games.

Being a male-on-male bondage publication, *Bound & Gagged* has a largely gay readership, but not at all an exclusively gay one. I am constantly amazed at the number of letters we get from readers who are not gay, but who are turned on by the idea of being tied up by or of tying up men. Equally amazing is the number of readers who have confessed to us that they were required to engage in sexual activity with fraternity brothers in the course of their hazings and initiations, even if they put it all behind them afterwards and never were tempted to do it again. I personally found this a little hard to believe myself at first, until I heard it over and over again from now happily married family men.

This is the first in what I hope will be a series of books on hazing practices. I invite those of you who ever underwent a hazing or an initiation to write me about your experiences. Tell me about them as they happened, without embellishments. Send them to me at The Outbound Press, 89 Fifth Avenue, Suite 803, New York, NY 10003.

Bob Wingate
Publisher